Awaken *your* Brain

Coming Alive
to **Vibrant Well-being**
and a **New Reality**

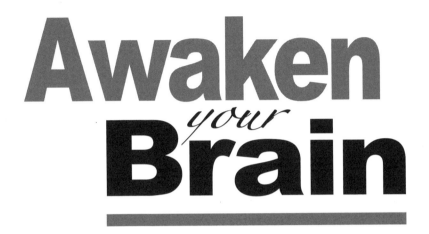

Awaken *your* Brain

Coming Alive
to Vibrant Well-being
and a New Reality

Jeff Skolnick MD PhD

SATORI WEST

Publishing

Published by SatoriWest Publishing, Seattle, WA 98126.

For quantity discounts please contact the publisher.

The publisher gratefully acknowledges permission to reprint material on pages 67-68 from the book, *The Power of Now,* © 1997 by Eckhart Tolle, pages 1-2. Reprinted with permission of New World Library, Novato, CA, www.newworld library.com.

Library of Congress Control Number: 2009904658
ISBN: 978-0-578-02329-8

Manufactured in the United States of America
First Edition

Editorial and production management by Alchemy West, Inc.
Robyn M Fritz MA MBA, president
Design/layout: Mi Ae Lipe, What Now Design
Editorial team: Jennifer Cassie, Laurel Robinson
Author photograph courtesy of Avriel Skolnick

Satori West Publishing is committed to preserving ancient forests and natural resources. We elected to print this title on 30% postconsumer recycled paper, processed chlorine-free. As a result, we have saved:

3 Trees (40' tall and 6-8" diameter)
2 Million BTUs of Total Energy
264 Pounds of Greenhouse Gases
1,196 Gallons of Wastewater
139 Pounds of Solid Waste

Satori West Publishing made this paper choice because our printer, Thomson-Shore, Inc., is a member of Green Press Initiative, a nonprofit program dedicated to supporting authors, publishers, and suppliers in their efforts to reduce their use of fiber obtained from endangered forests.

For more information, visit www.greenpressinitiative.org

Environmental impact estimates were made using the Environmental Defense Paper Calculator. For more information visit: www.edf.org/papercalculator

For my dear children,
Sandler and Avriel

Contents

Acknowledgments / ix

Preface / xi

Part 1: Introduction to Neural-Wellness Inshifting (NWI): Genesis and Gist

1. Why This Book, This Approach / 3
2. My Journey / 11
3. Peak Well-being and a Great Life / 21

Part 2: The Realities of You

4. Levels of Reality / 29
5. The Dream or Nightmare Reality / 33
6. The "Something's Wrong With Your Brain" Reality / 35
7. The Daydreaming Reality / 37
8. The Willingly Suspended State of Reality / 39
9. The Ordinary, Relative World Reality / 41
10. The Awakened, Absolute World Reality / 57
11. The Road to Awakening / 65

Part 3: Brain Science

12. The Mind and Brain Problem / 73
13. An Amazing Organ / 79
14. The Seeds of Your Higher Brain: A Hypothesis / 85
15. The Neurosoteriology Model / 93

Part 4: The Skill of Neural Inshifting

16. Inshifting Scenarios / 107
17. The Process of Neural Inshifting / 111
18. The Neural Inshifting Steps: An Overview / 121
19. Step 1: Energize and Release / 131
20. Step 2: Grounding and Loosening / 139
21. Step 3: Splitting and Detaching / 151
22. Step 4: Openness and Power / 163
23. Step 5: Just Knowing, Spontaneously Flowing / 175
24. Neural Inshifting: Summing Up / 191

Part 5: Wellness Inshifting

25. In Pursuit of Wellness / 207
26. The LifePlan for Awakening / 215
27. Physical Inshifting: Health and a Natural High / 219
28. Mental Inshifting: Control and Insight / 235
29. Social Inshifting: Empowering Connections / 271
30. Cultural Inshifting: Success and Acceptance / 281
31. Moral Inshifting: Principles and Purpose / 299
32. Spiritual Inshifting: Ancient Rites, Modern Practice / 309

Afterword: The Journey to Awakening / 335

Glossary / 339

Bibliography / 345

Acknowledgments

Ten years in the making, this book has been like a third sibling to my children. Thank you for your sacrifice, the extent to which you will never know. Thanks also to Robyn Fritz, my editor, book packager and constant cheerleader for your stalwart optimism and confidence. Thanks also to Mi Ae Lipe for layout and design, and to Jennifer Cassie and Laurel Robinson for proofreading. To the many Zen teachers who have helped me along the way from Gainesville, Florida, to the Zen Centers in Los Angeles, Chicago and here in Seattle at Dai Bai Zan Cho Bo Zen Temple, with its Abbot and my longtime friend, Genjo Marinello: deep gassho (bow of gratitude). Thanks also to Rosalind Franklin University/The Chicago Medical School for creating a dual psychiatry residency and doctoral program in neuropsychology, which allowed me to explore mind and brain issues and create my own model. I also appreciate Rabbi Michael Latz, my other family and friends, and my colleagues at SatoriWest, who gave feedback on my book, its various names and versions.

Thank you, finally, to my mom, whose dedication to cure her brother of severe mental illness led her on a journey into alternative health care, wellness, psychology and psychiatry, leading me on my journey inward.

Preface

*I*magine, you're driving to the airport to pick up a dear, elderly aunt you haven't seen in a long time. You wanted to leave early, but were delayed. Still, you're okay, you're making good time, you can just make the flight as it arrives ... and then you see it a short distance away. Traffic is backed up and there's no way to evade it. Panic and frustration set in, and as you slow down, your irritation and agitation start mounting. There's no way to notify them at the airport. You're ready to make more aggressive moves to get through by weaving from one lane to another ... when you remember. You learned to inshift.

Switching direction in how you process energy, and in how you experience and manage mind and body, a significant change begins setting in. The anger, sadness and stress loosen their control over you. You release the tense energy that is draining you while you draw it up as fresh energy into your head. You're becoming more alert and relaxed, detached, yet present and vividly aware of the total scenario of this moment: the experience of you sitting in your car driving, the image in your mind of your aunt getting off the plane disappointed that she doesn't see you, the sadness and frustration you feel, the sight of cars around you stuck in traffic, the feelings of the stresses of the day—the whole package, just exactly the way it is, defining the uniqueness of this singular moment in time.

Pulling your attention further away the most prominent feature of your experience is that you are strikingly more aware of the fact that you are alive this moment. A sense of well-being begins bubbling up within you. Sure the deeper feeling of frustration, sadness and disappointment is still there but it is felt and expressed so fully it feels liberating! You begin to fluidly move to negotiate the traffic and the *events in your mind, all of which now seem to flow more from one moment to the next.*

Context shines through: "This is a stressful moment but it's not personal, not a statement about my luck. It's one in an ocean of other life moments, one of the ups and downs of living." You realize you may look back on this time and remember it someday as horrible, maybe, but representative of the incredible run of having been alive.

As you logically plan and run through future scenarios you deduce that someone will be there to assist your aunt. Then as you imagine her worrying, an intuitive insight becomes crystal clear to you: you know her, she knows how excited you are to see her and she's savvy enough to figure out that you could've been delayed in traffic.

Everything in your senses, body and mind becomes more vivid and whole, seeming to be new and less real. Life becomes more ironic. Appreciation wells up. You wait with excitement (and frustration) to see your aunt one amazing moment at a time . . .

Imagine what your life would be like if there was contentment below any frustration, a level of tranquility at the root of any fear, and a profound appreciation as the backdrop to any dissatisfaction.

This book will take you on a new kind of journey, one of healing and advanced development, one that has the potential to change your life. Yet this particular approach is different than many others you may have heard of before, because the journey is directed sharply inward, beyond the recesses of your own mind, into your brain, to the point that it Awakens! It's a way of life and of healing and well-being that offers you a better way of being in the world in "boring" and ordinary moments as well as in extraordinary times and in crises. It shows you how to fulfill the highest aspirations of what has been called spiritual attainment while you heal from a world that conditions you to stress.

I call this new approach to life neural-wellness inshifting (NWI). Inshifting is a way to more fully access your higher brain areas, and in so doing, re-direct the attention and control your lower brain commands. It's a way to enter into a world flowing with presence away from a world obsessed with the information values of your senses, body, mind and reactions. It's a world of higher states of awareness, higher levels of reality and inner ways of being!

I have glimpsed this new level of reality firsthand because I've been developing and practicing this skill for years. As a psychiatrist with a doctorate in natural health with advanced training in neuropsychology, and as a 28-year Zen Buddhist meditator, I believe strongly in this approach to mental and physical wellness and higher states of being. And just like everyone else, I continually use this approach as I struggle with insecurity, anger, disappointment and a continual desire for more. It helps me a great deal and fosters my ongoing growth and development. In one form or another, inshifting has helped dozens of my patients over the years deal with the harshest manifestations of psychiatric illnesses there are. I'm certain it can help you as well.

This book will show you how. Beginning in Part 1, Introduction to Neural-Wellness Inshifting (NWI): Genesis and Gist, it provides a comprehensive overview of the development and premises of its concepts, as well as the issues you and I and most of humanity face in life. Part 2, The Realities of You, offers a look at different levels of reality your brain could and does enter daily by inshifting, while Part 3, Brain Science, reviews the brain models behind inshifting. Part 4, The Skill of Neural Inshifting, delves into the centerpiece of this approach—the five steps of neural inshifting. Part 5, Wellness Inshifting, outlines the crucial practices from different areas of life that make this skill much easier to learn or to happen naturally.

The skill of neural inshifting includes but moves beyond the now widely touted and researched concept of mindfulness. It offers not only a science-based model of how the brain and mind work but steps that take you more directly along a path to Awakening. Along with the diverse life and wellness principles and practices that support neural inshifting—many contemporary, some ancient—NWI actually integrates diverse wellness practices, strategies and skills. In essence, the model is one of total wellness brought together and coordinated by a "spiritually" based understanding of the brain.

While many books explore mindfulness meditation, science and holistic wellness, this one uniquely points to the inescapable fact that floating up there in your head right now is an organ whose higher parts can do more, be more and experience more than the narrow, ordinary "you" of its lower parts can ever experience.

The problem is that we have higher brain areas that humanity as a species has not accessed nearly as much as they could be. That puts lower brain areas in control—an unhealthy and potentially dangerous condition that has innumerable manifestations. Not only are the Spanish Inquisition, Holocaust, September 11 massacres and all suicides of otherwise healthy people indicative of the suggestibility and programmable power of your lower brain, but so are the generations of people who have lived and died unfulfilled.

Your brain can be trained to expand beyond this condition, beyond your normal view of life, beyond your normal self. This book will show you that there is actually a higher "you" that you are not fully in touch with. It exists in a higher state of reality that has been called cosmic consciousness, nirvana, enlightenment, heaven within or (and what I refer to as) Awakening. This is just one reality in a spectrum of brain realities. When you learn how to train and master your brain by inshifting, you can move a long way towards what is simply the highest stage of development and level of experience humans can reach.

My task is to show you a new world of possibility, a practical world explained with a 21st-century perspective. Using this approach to total wellness, with multiple practices specifically geared to boost the skill of neural inshifting, you can open up worlds that were often accessible only by surviving a crisis or by intensive lifelong religious or spiritual practice.

The entire NWI approach (the brain skill plus its wellness practices) begins with healing, with fixing the built-in deficiencies that can put your brain out of control and cause you discomfort, difficulties, stress and ill health. Yet, it culminates in the possibility for great well-being and happiness, in knowing who (or what) you really are, and in feeling profoundly connected and radically amazed with life.

If you are willing to work at this formula, you'll begin to steadily and perceptibly Awaken to a life endlessly fascinating and meaningful, filled—no matter what happens—with an inner peace and contentment and likely dotted with moments of ecstasy.

As a physician and psychiatrist I hope you'll keep in mind that NWI is not just a luxury, a path to ecstatic higher states—it's a practical necessity in life! Those higher states are the very definition of mental health and physical well-being. The alternative is some degree of life dissatisfaction, stress and illness, if not misery, suffering and premature death. Dealing with your inner self and higher brain is needed to be able to make any area of human wellness and personal growth pay off and last. Clearly, this is the most vital skill and way of living that you can ever learn, fulfilling your greatest potential. Mastering your brain is inarguably the most important journey you can take in life.

Before I conclude this Preface and let you dive in to this material, I need to emphasize and clarify a few points to correct any misconceptions, because the approach offered in this book is unlike most other self-improvement models.

First, the NWI model can quicken the ancient quest for

Awakening and its associated peak levels of wellness and well-being. Yet, this is not necessarily a quick and easy approach—it just has the potential to be quicker and easier than many other methods used in the past. The deepest results are not going to be instantaneous, although immediate results are likely.

Nor is this "spirituality and wellness for dummies." Thinking, struggle, understanding, practice and persistence are required, as in any acquired skill, which is why I'm creating a wellness organization to support it.

NWI comes with many balances, such as effort and non-effort, energy and relaxation, engagement and detachment. One balance in particular is seemingly paradoxical (until you experience it). This is absolutely a book on self-improvement, a five-step brain skill, with dozens of wellness strategies necessary to reach a goal. Yet, the end result is to be able to accept, appreciate and be amazed by every single thing about yourself and the world around you, "good" or "bad," exactly and precisely the way they are, without the need to improve or change a thing!

In other words, as confusing as it may seem at first, these are some of the paradoxes of the NWI model. It helps you create the goal of detaching from goals so that goals flow more naturally, or detach from thinking so that thoughts flow more intuitively, or master intention without action so that correct action becomes spontaneous, or transcend who you are so that you can be more authentically yourself.

So get ready, put on your "thinking cap," and let's dive in. And may all our journeys be fruitful.

Jeff Skolnick, MD, PhD
Seattle, Washington
June 2009

Part 1

Introduction to
Neural-Wellness Inshifting (NWI):
Genesis and Gist

Doesn't everything die at last, and too soon?
Tell me, what is it you plan to do
with your one wild and precious life?

— *Mary Oliver* —

It is not half as important to burn the midnight oil as it
is to be awake in the daytime.

— *E. W. Elmore* —

1

Why This Book, This Approach

*Life to the great majority is only a constant struggle for
mere existence, with the certainty of losing it at last.*

— *Arthur Schopenhauer* —

*The life force is vigorous.
The delight that accompanies it counterbalances
all the pains and hardships that confront men.*

— *W. Somerset Maugham* —

This book is different in many ways from other books on human healing, personal growth and higher development. In part, that's because it is centered around the ancient practice of meditation—the group of skills that has brought extraordinary healing and life-opening experiences to so many people for millennia. What makes this book distinctly different is that it redefines meditation in the 21st-century language of the brain, based on my original model of how the mind and brain work. That model has generated a new brain skill called neural inshifting.

As I mentioned in the Preface, neural inshifting is likely the most important skill you can learn in life. Learning it literally means the difference between stress and inner peace, struggle and inner contentment, an ordinary existence and an extraordinary experience of life.

This book is also predicated on the novel concept that this important skill of neural inshifting organizes and integrates wellness practices from a wide range of areas—physical, mental, social, cultural (daily living), moral (principles and mission) and traditionally spiritual! When you learn to master your brain you can bring yourself vibrant health, happiness and peace, empowering relationships, material success, integrity and purpose, and the realization of so-called "spiritual" levels of understanding, experience and behavior. You can also use any successes in those areas to help you better master your brain: that is the neural-wellness inshifting (NWI) approach that sets this book apart from many other approaches to wellness.

After many years of experimentation on myself, formal practice and wide-ranging training, I discovered that human healing and higher development are much easier once you understand that you have an underused higher brain that can do, be and experience more than you realize, and that who you ordinarily experience yourself to be is not the highest stage of being "you."

It is very unfortunate that most of us do not know how to train our brains to expand beyond the commonplace, stressful reality of our daily lives. Billions of people who have ever lived, the masses of people Henry David Thoreau described as "living lives of quiet desperation," indeed, the vast majority of us, have not taken advantage of the healing and growth engendered by the simplicity of this single fact: that our higher brain areas are considerably underused. However, the fact remains: there is a higher "you." And it exists in a state of reality religious and spiritual thinkers and scientists alike have referred to by different names, but which I call "Awakening." Simply put, Awakening, far from being a myth, is the reality of a well-trained brain and a higher stage of psychosocial-spiritual brain development.

Does the fact that there is a higher "you" that you haven't yet experienced seem like a radical statement? For most people this idea may seem crazy. Yet it has been discovered and rediscovered by generations of religious and secular self-explorers—some intentionally, some by accident. For them, Awakening was not only the answer to the inherent stress, emotional challenges and disappointments of living a human life, it was also the discovery of a heaven-like place within, not "out there." As you will learn, cosmic consciousness, nirvana, enlightenment, grace, heaven within, paradise on Earth, Awakening, or whatever you choose to call it, is a real phenomenon and practically anyone can achieve it.

At this point the healthy skeptic in you may be wondering if these states are more myth than truth, or more likely to be discovered by spiritual seekers who are willing to spend a lifetime searching for a far-off mystical reality—not for people who lead busy lives in modern times. After all, how could it be worth reading a self-help book that proposes you learn to heal and find success in life by discovering an exceptional but elusive place within you? Is it really necessary to use Awakening as the goal of brain development rather than solely using what most people might consider down-to-earth, practical skills?

Learning to Awaken your brain by inshifting *is* practical and *is* meant to be used every day and in every way to help you function better, heal mind and body, and transform your life. Nothing is more practical or more important than that. The NWI approach opens up that world of possibility, that gift within.

So, what in general is this brain skill of neural inshifting that sets this book apart? It's a way of shifting energy, attention and control around in your brain so that you find an inner mastery and way of experiencing and a higher way of being. This evolved stage comes from your brain's ability to experience and appreciate how unique and amazing the fact of "its" aliveness is as that unfolds in each unique moment, while it spontaneously and authentically flows with life. That's what I refer to as being "inshifted."

More specifically, what happens is that your higher brain is accessed when the locus of your control and the focus of your awareness shifts to an inner spot experienced in the center of your head. I call it Point X. The Hindus call it the inner eye or third eye. When you discover it, work out of it and become it, your experience, your way of functioning and your reality change.

Granted, neural inshifting, being a five-step process (with several sub-steps), *can* be tricky to learn, slippery to hang on to and complicated to master. This is not exactly "Brain Mastery for Dummies." If it were simple, many more people would be Awakened by now. It *does* take time and patience, just like learning any new skill, except you can't see this skill because it resides within you. To do it, you need to learn how to let go of the usual, habitual ways you have been in the world so that you can transcend the usual "you." It is difficult, yes, but pleasurable and freeing, unlike anything else you can experience, well worth the effort it takes to learn it and strengthen it with wellness. When you can transform out of the common or ordinary reality that drives you to competitiveness or helplessness, that makes you crave and relentlessly desire things and fleeting pleasures and run from anything uncomfortable, that keeps you alienated within yourself, stuck in harmful habits and unhealthy personality traits making you insecure and fearful of aging and losing control—when you lose all that, that is called liberation. It's another side to Awakening. When you inshift into Point X, gradually or suddenly, your life starts to change for the better, in ways you might not have predicted.

While you may be intrigued by this prospect of this book, you may also be thinking that inshifting might be *too* complicated and difficult to learn; otherwise, wouldn't everybody be Awakened? (Pick up a newspaper and you'll see that clearly they're not.) You may also believe that people can be completely fulfilled and successful without learning to inshift to any great extent. Besides, isn't life really about learning to cope with difficulty, and isn't your life good enough the way it is?

From the vantage point of the ordinary reality of most un-Awakened people, unless you are acutely aware of being miserable, some people's lives might seem good enough, or at least filled with a steady stream of distractions that make them feel content. Yet when people inshift just enough to experience even a bit of Awakening, they often tell of having never realized how unfulfilled their lives were in comparison, how unnecessarily they struggled and suffered. (Like an adult looking back on their adolescent years!) It is that realization that begins the healing process espoused by this book.

Again, the healthy skeptic in you may be thinking that it is an exaggeration to say that almost everyone struggles, stresses and suffers in life, regardless of how outwardly successful they may seem. Yet, understanding this observation in other people will help you more fully understand it better in yourself (if you aren't already acutely aware of it). Poets (like Thoreau), philosophers, behavioral scientists and the major religions have been calling attention to the "human condition" for a very long time. Buddhists in particular have been exploring this question since the time of Siddhartha Gautama over two thousand years ago. He described this same observation embodied by his now famous axiom (and Buddhist First Noble Truth): "Life *is* suffering." (Unless you're Awakened, of course.) The axiom has been interpreted in modern terms as "life is at minimum uncomfortable, difficult and stressful, even if you are outwardly successful," and, yes, often more than many people fully realize.

If you are in crisis, grieving, recovering from trauma or struggling with serious health, financial or relationship issues, you will immediately get this, if only until the crisis is over. Others will still probably protest and emphatically say, "I'm not suffering or even uncomfortable. I'm looking for self-improvement, for success and greater happiness, but there's nothing disabling or uncontrollably stressful about my life. Of course, life has ups and downs, but I'm satisfied enough and handle things okay."

Consider yourself, though, through the eyes of the statistician. The data show that despite their socioeconomic status, Americans and citizens of other developed countries are experiencing a lower quality of life and an increase in endemic stress. This has led to a host of conditions, including epidemic insomnia, irritability, higher rates of clinical depression and anxiety, addictions, divorce, lifestyle-related physical illnesses, exhaustion and obesity.

A Seattle TV station recently conducted a poll in which 60-80% of households reported that they were disorganized in home, car, equipment maintenance and personal records; made impulsive purchases and poor consumer decisions; and were confused about finances, investing and taxes. We also know that Americans are increasingly uncertain about what happiness is and question values and meaning, principles, goals and higher purpose: hence, the burgeoning billion-dollar self-improvement industry. Many people and families increasingly feel lonely and alienated, indicative not only of the disappearance of small towns and extended family households, but of a culture that fosters lower brain programming that causes you to feel separate from others.

If you are excluded from all of the above, consider yourself fortunate. Not so your neighbors and others around you. But what is it about the configuration of our brain that makes us so stressed? Is it just because we don't access our higher brain enough? There's another side to that imbalance: our lower brain areas dominate the higher ones.

That's been the case since the beginning of human history. Yet even more so today, as I mentioned before, our lower brains prevail over us because of the conditions of modern culture. There are many reasons why people are set up to struggle and stress. We haven't, for instance, learned to counterbalance and control our technology and consumer-driven economy, so artificial sweeteners and TV shows are able to force our brains toward immediate pleasures over more natural sources of happiness. Corporate marketing unchecked by our own higher awareness often makes us more susceptible to unhealthy desires over enlightened values. Our lower brain areas, which include our minds, become programmed to make most of us feel that life should be fair, when it is not, and that we are unhappy and stressed because we are victimized by life circumstances, when we are not.

One of the more fundamental issues that put a damper on our psychospiritual growth is this oppressive dynamic in our brain: the higher brain has evolved the capacity to be self-aware, yet because it is still dominated by the lower brain, that acute awareness gives us "existential angst." At some point in your life you increasingly feel it as grief, a dread or sadness about eventually losing everything you cherish, including yourself. Many people just feel it deep down, not realizing what it is, as an anxious need to stop time, or as sadness or fear.

It's little wonder that stress is so endemic in human civilization. From predictable stage-of-life crises to the burgeoning industry in "anti-aging" therapies and cosmetic surgery, lower brain control predisposes us to need healing.

We can learn how to meet whatever stresses affect our lives and turn them into opportunities for healing, growth and even transformative experiences. The skill of neural inshifting and the entire NWI approach provide modern solutions to an age-old malady. This book, if practiced and not just read, can begin your journey to heal and Awaken, opening up a world of new possibilities for freedom and happiness.

2

My Journey

Man must sit in chair with mouth open
for very long time before roast duck fly in.

— *Chinese proverb* —

When I was 10 my uncle became progressively and profoundly mentally ill. A normal, outgoing, highly intelligent child, he started having extreme mood swings in his late teens that culminated in rages, nonsensical thinking, paranoia and hallucinations. He died young.

As his illness progressed, my mother, desperate to find a cure for him and relieve their parents' numbing heartache, explored many avenues to cure him. She researched different psychological approaches, new psychiatric medications and, when nothing else worked, alternative health care and medicine, including health-promoting diets, fasting, exercise, supplementation and stress reduction, to name a few. She often incorporated her growing knowledge base into our family's life.

That's how psychology and natural health became dual interests of mine. In my teens I read psychology books, mainly self-help, and began thinking a lot about health and self-exploration. In high school I experienced one seminal moment that became a crossroad in creating the basic premise of this book: I read a chapter in a psychology textbook that speculated about the nature of consciousness. The author wondered how organized chemicals, no matter how complexly arranged, could become alive, and not only that, but aware!

I was riveted by that idea. I still am. Contemplating it has given me greater clarity about the incredibleness of what it means to have a brain that knows it's alive. If you let go of your intellect and stop and contemplate that question, you will realize that "who" you believe you are is really the result of the complex activity of nothing more than a body organ, similar to your other body organs. Biological tissue. You are a process, not a permanent thing. Your experience of being you is what Albert Einstein called "an illusion of consciousness"; there is no real stable identity that is "you." "You" are the projection generated by neural (brain) tissue that gives the experience of you. Sense that and you will experience a degree of Awakening and of liberation!

The more I read the more I wanted to be a psychologist and study consciousness. I also decided to become a physician after touring the Hope hospital ship in Miami Beach, an enormous floating hospital that travels the globe delivering modern medical care to needy people in developing countries. Psychiatry was the compromise.

While I was in college majoring in biology and psychology a friend introduced me to Zen Buddhism. It is a meditative practice and system of direct inner experience that can actually be considered as much an empirical scientific method as a religion. Zen relegates the trappings of religious dogma, universal cosmologies and rituals to the backseat, putting self-knowing first and foremost.

For me, the resonance was quick and deep. Zen Buddhism united psychology and consciousness with my inclination to self-exploration and interests in natural wellness and higher psycho-spiritual development. As a result, I have practiced one form or another of Zen Buddhism daily for almost three decades (including neural inshifting, which is an adaptation of it). I have read dozens of books and other literature on Zen and other meditations, Buddhist psychology, Eastern spirituality, secular spirituality, psychology and the neuropsychology of consciousness.

Using the reports of advanced meditators and that accumulated knowledge, I developed a model that described the changes I myself experienced over time, along with the wellness practices I experimented with to enhance those skills. That model and those practices helped me overcome many of the obstacles that people face in a meditation practice.

What are those obstacles? Why wasn't the traditional meditative path enough for me?

One reason was that the meditative instructions I received were confusing. Most citizens of developed countries have technology-induced attention deficit, and I have more than my share, so when the practice was to sit rock still for extended periods of time, getting clear instructions was that much more critical. I now realize in retrospect that this and all the instructions were totally valid. They were just confusing, less than fully helpful and, I now believe, unnecessarily difficult.

For example, it wasn't explained that when you reach a level of inshifting ability, so that your inner control is strong, you don't want to move. No force is needed. By not moving you are mimicking that state and fooling your brain into inshifting. If I had known that, it would have helped.

Another example was the instruction about posture found in the book that I revered, and still revere, *Zen Mind, Beginner's Mind,* by Shunryu Suzuki. It mentions that an important aspect of meditation is to sit cross-legged or otherwise in an erect, balanced and grounded posture, because it reflects the internal "mind" posture. He didn't say physical posture made it *easier,* he said posture was part of the meditation. I thought that meant that to meditate you *must* sit still with an erect posture. It implied that you couldn't live your life in a meditative state. I knew there was such a thing as walking meditation, but it seemed like a special case of a very controlled but moving erect posture. How was that going to help me in my daily life, when I needed to move around freely and function? Again, I realize now that an erect and balanced posture brings energy to your higher brain. It also puts the brain into a state where the higher brain is used more than the lower. But it is not required to meditate. In fact, Awakenings are often found in less than ideal circumstances, such as crises and illness.

I was also instructed that one way to meditate was "just sitting" and being in the moment. That instruction was just too vague for me. I interpreted it as being aware of my body and senses without thinking. It implied that I shouldn't think and that my thinking was *not* also part of the moment, which I now believe is not true.

If that form of meditation was too difficult, I was to be aware of and count my breaths as an anchor to being in the moment. If my mind wandered, I was to continually bring it back to my breathing. The task of counting my breaths was particularly hard because it stressed me to pay so much attention to one activity. Sure, I realize now that *how* one pays attention—gently, not defining "failure" and expecting and welcoming a degree of body and mind stress—is more important than how much attention you pay.

I also believed that the mark of a good meditator was how long you could stay focused on counting breaths, how many cycles of ten you could manage, without getting distracted into thought and fantasy.

I no longer believe that is true, either. Back then, counting breaths became for me an exercise in doing it perfectly to get the prize of an Awakening; it was a dream project for anyone seeking to *strengthen* the mind's dominance, not weaken its grip! Meditation, early on, became a practice of either thinking about what it was like to be in the moment or observing my breaths and thinking about not slipping up. Either way I exerted a lot of effort. If mind wandering is seen as a sign of failure, even that becomes another way to strengthen the mind by using it to judge and interpret. Not so helpful. It took many years before I understood why "slipping up" was impossible, and why force is not needed or useful.

In other Zen groups, as in some secular mindfulness programs offered today, I was instructed to watch the "parade of thoughts and feelings go by" while meditating, which included the idea of an "I." Who then would be "watching" the parade if it wasn't the "me" that I know as me? Where was this ego or sense of "I" if not the normal "me"? The only instrument I knew of at the time to watch myself with was my mind. No one said that you can function in life without relying on your mind. No one indicated that there was an inner place that you could literally feel inside your head from which you could experience things, including your mind and other lower brain activity. And that this actually made you more adept in life.

I was warned that the boredom and frustration that arose were signs of unconsciousness coming to consciousness, and that observing this was good. I definitely sat with a lot of impatience and frustration. I just had nowhere from which to observe the frustration except from my mind, which created the frustration in the first place. I do believe that I actually grew from that, but I think it also took a toll on me. It's one thing to challenge yourself. It's another to be masochistic.

It would have been more helpful to regularly talk about what I was experiencing. That would have clarified my mistakes and kept me from excessive frustration and from using force and thought to be present in the moment. I would have learned to experience from an inner place. You see, it is easy to slip into thinking about experiencing rather than to just experience. Forcing yourself not to think won't at all prevent you from thinking. It makes you rely on thinking even more. It would also have been a humane source of encouragement and validation to learn that some struggle is good and necessary and not a sign of failure. That may have been mentioned, yet it isn't the same as having it modeled and sharing it with others.

Besides "right practice" emphasizing posture, there are other ways to make all that sitting and focusing inward easier. Buddhist canon does describe "right living," "right attitude" and "right understanding" as practices integral to meditation. It just wasn't bridged to the mushrooming self-help and wellness industry that could have made my meditation much easier.

When I began to elucidate the practice of neural inshifting it clarified the meditative skill in tangible ways that can be felt, with concrete steps as opposed to philosophical terms that are open to interpretation. It related Awakening to normal development and to what is happening in the brain more than to cryptic ideas and metaphors that I believe serve more to confuse people than clarify. (That being said, too much description encourages a reliance on thinking that doesn't help, either.) Neural inshifting was also designed to bring you closer to the point of Awakening.

For instance, meditation instructions did not seem the same as what was described as an experience of Awakening. To me, they should be. For example, according to the Buddhist Heart Sutra, meditation leads to "emptiness":

> ... So, in emptiness, there is no body,
> no feeling, no thought,
> no will, no consciousness.
> There are no eyes, no ears,
> no nose, no tongue,
> no body, no mind.
> There is no seeing, no hearing,
> no smelling, no tasting,
> no touching, no imagining.
> There is nothing seen, nor heard,
> nor smelled, nor tasted,
> nor touched, nor imagined ...

The Heart Sutra tells of a state of emptiness that results from meditation. Why then instruct meditators to focus on breathing as their entire practice when the desire is to reach a state where there is no particular focus, as in "no body, no seeing"? It took many years for me to understand that a state of emptiness will eventually come about as the result of any mindfulness practice or focus. I felt that there could have been instructions that were more explicit and led to a state of emptiness and presence more directly, rather than indirectly.

Again, neural inshifting addresses that.

I loved Zen practice with its obtuse parables and directions. It was exciting and mystical. Yet, excitement and mysticism cannot be relied on as a source of motivation. Why? Because they strengthen the mind in its desire for adventure and in visions of otherworldliness. Yet that is what kept me going, because I had nothing concrete to hold on to. I thought I was the only one struggling so much. It would have helped enormously to know that everyone else was struggling, too. And so I've incorporated the NWI approach into an organization I call SatoriWest Center for Advanced Living and Wellness; its main structure is its LifeClub.

After finishing medical school I entered a psychiatry residency training program that also offered a doctorate in neuropsychology (the study of the brain as it creates experience and behavior). It seemed perfect. It was a way to study the brain, consciousness and meditation, an opportunity to explain meditation to myself in neuropsychological terms and provide more clarity for me and others. I wanted to write a dissertation on a subject directly related to consciousness. Unfortunately, like many doctorate programs, the faculty encourages what they are knowledgeable and interested in. So I completed the psychiatric training program and most of the neuropsychology course work and left the program to continue working on my own.

Yet, during that program I began working on a model of what happens in the brain subjectively and behaviorally as we meditate. That early model described the meditative process that takes you from normal to spiritual levels. I later expanded it to encompass a wider spectrum of human behavior and experience, from the most primitive and pathological ways of being in the world through the common, "normal" or ordinary reality that most of us live in, up to the highest, most Awakened states. I called this model neurosoteriology. I finished it as the dissertation requirement for a doctorate in natural health. It is one of the cornerstones of this book.

After psychiatry residency training, I worked with chronically and severely mentally ill people in public hospitals and clinics, putting aside my experiences and training in meditation, as well as my thinking about the neurosoteriology model, and even my education in natural health. I started a part-time private psychiatric practice with higher functioning people with less severe mental illnesses.

That's the point when it all came together for me. I realized firsthand the common theme of their struggles: their lower brain's dominance over their lives. What were the areas in those patients' lives that were most affected by this dominance? As we'll explore further in the next chapter, some of those issues are the high incidence of low self-esteem, impaired relationships, financial mismanagement and anxieties, home and life disorganization, unclear values and a lack of spiritual direction, to name a few. Why were all these areas affected? Because the more control the lower brain has over the higher brain, the more impulsive, inflexible, fatigued, dysfunctional, unwell and disorganized you will be.

An even more relevant question was whether my patients were really all that different from me and everyone else in society. Hardly, as we'll explore further on.

I started using the neurosoteriology model with these private practice patients and with other patients with severe and persistent mental illnesses in hospitals and mental health clinics. However, explaining the issues and offering guidance on meditation to remedy their imbalanced brains were not sufficient. They needed what I needed: a skill that was more tangible and comprehensible, that could be used anywhere and any time, and that tracked progression from healing to higher development. More than that, they needed that skill to be the center of a life and total wellness approach.

That's when the neural and wellness aspects of inshifting crystallized.

I created a series of workshops covering several wellness areas with like-minded colleagues before I realized even *that* wouldn't be enough! People need more than education, more than individual workshops, to make significant gains in neural inshifting and sizable inroads in the lifestyle approaches that support it. They need a complete organization that offers them key ingredients critical for human change: a culture they can belong to that supports their efforts, a small group (tribe) that they can identify with, individual coaching, professional guidance and workshops, retreats, a place to practice meditation and fitness when not at home, and so on. That has led me to design SatoriWest's Life-Club, and I wrote this book to launch it.

The implication of this notion of an organization that can bring NWI to life is important for you to understand before you embark on this journey inward. The issue is that you can read this book and practice neural inshifting on your own, implement the LifePlan for Awakening, or LifePlan, found in Part 5 and the various wellness strategies geared to help you inshift, and you will be successful enough to see a positive change in your life. Yet we are not islands. We need each other. We need real-time human help, coaching, community—all of those elements I mentioned above—to make the leaps that can lead to a fully Awakened life.

Since we've introduced the higher and lower brain and the skill of inshifting that changes their balance, let's next introduce the idea that wellness practices can foster inshifting.

3

Peak Well-being and a Great Life

We didn't all come over on the same ship,
but we were all in the same boat.

— *Bernard M. Baruch* —

Millionaires rarely smile.

— *Andrew Carnegie* —

The wise men of antiquity, when they wished to make the
whole world peaceful and happy, first put their own States
into proper order. Before putting their own States into
proper order, they regulated their own families.
Before regulating their families, they regulated themselves.
Before regulating themselves, they tried to be sincere in their
thoughts. Before being sincere in their thoughts, they tried to
see things exactly as they really were.

— *Confucius* —

We've explored Awakening as a cure for the built-in dysfunction that comes with a human brain. In Part 2, The Realities of You, we'll talk more about Awakening as a stage of development that comes with incredible experiences. But what do Awakening and inshifting have to do with making your everyday life better? And how can aspects of your everyday life help you inshift and Awaken? Part 5, Wellness Inshifting, addresses these issues more fully. Let's introduce them here with a simple yet profound question: what do you want out of your life?

If you made a list of the first things that pop into your mind about what you want out of your relatively short stint on Earth, what would it include?

If you're like most people you first want physical wellness. You want to be healthy, to heal from illnesses and injuries, to have vitality and abundant energy and a sharp mind with good memory. Of course you want this for your entire, long life, and to never suffer from old age, infirmity or pain.

Even with modern technology, natural health and alternative medicine, true physical wellness is only possible when you are mentally well. How could you be energized from the right diet and in peak shape from exercise and yet be unable to sleep because you're worried and anxious? How well will your body be when you hold on to anger and resentment for years, or if you're stressed and plagued by low self-esteem and self-doubt?

How does mental wellness play a role in physical wellness? Think of this: if the human mind can make your skin blister under hypnosis (which it can), if a placebo can cause the same cures and side effects as modern medications, then your mind can greatly affect your health. People can lose the will to live because of illness or despair. That's the immense potential of the mind, and the importance of mental wellness. Are there aspects of mental wellness on your list?

Having mental wellness means being able to weather the ups and downs of life with humor and perspective; to have self-esteem and like yourself exactly as you are while striving for self-improvement; to solve problems rationally and intuitively; to learn and improve every day because you have the self-esteem to appreciate and learn from mistakes; to be self-confident and optimistic; to feel solid and mature because you don't take everything personally; and to live with fond nostalgia for the enjoyable parts of your life instead of being mired in resentment, sadness and regret.

Just as physical wellness requires mental wellness, the opposite is true: mental wellness requires physical wellness in return.

How could you find laughter, wisdom and perspective if you are physically drained, strained and depleted?

Yet, mental wellness requires some degree of social wellness. It is hard to imagine feeling psychologically very sound without some amount of love, support and nurturing, without being able to negotiate with people to solve problems, or stand up for your rights in difficult situations. With social wellness you can create and enjoy deep intimacy with the people you choose to be closest to—with trust and affection, sharing laughter, fun and painful times while still maintaining boundaries. More than just people closest to you, social wellness entails seeing and celebrating the value in all humanity. Anything on your list here?

Of course, social wellness requires mental wellness in return. Imagine being in a great community and in a loving, wonderful relationship while also in the throes of depression or being run down and fatigued.

What makes it easier to have social wellness? How about the ability to successfully negotiate society, which we'll call cultural wellness?

I'll bet there are many things on your list from this area. Do you dream of financial success or, at least, of financial independence? Do you hope to achieve something significant, whether in a career, profession or personal interest, such as sports, travel or a hobby? Do you want to better negotiate and organize the tasks of daily living and planning? How about being prepared for natural disasters, accidents and downturns in health and fortune? Cultural wellness is being able to organize yourself, accomplish tasks, get educated in diverse areas of life, make wise decisions, learn from your mistakes and make better decisions. It takes social, mental and physical wellness in return.

So, what could be next in the chain of wellnesses? Moral wellness. To be morally well means living a life of meaning and altruistic purpose in accordance with your highest principles. An altruistic purpose could be the desire to make the world a better place by working for social justice or bringing beauty to others' lives. Moral wellness requires the ability to know right from wrong, to know what is and is not in your highest interests, to have values and ethics that bring happiness and fairness to the world, and to be a righteous person because it feels good. Were there elements of moral wellness on your list?

So how does cultural wellness relate to moral wellness? Quite a bit, actually. Having moral character will increase your chances of achieving and sustaining success in society. Living according to moral principles enhanced with social skills will generate goodwill for you to succeed at your life's mission. It is easier to pursue your life's altruistic purpose if you are organized and knowledgeable about the ways of the world. How fulfilling could it be to become successful, have a tight-knit family, boost your self-esteem, or attain greater health by violating the rights and feelings of others?

Like the other wellnesses, moral wellness is a goal in and of itself. It's empowering, stabilizing and practical because understanding your values allows you to better prioritize them.

What's next? Spiritual wellness.

Spiritual wellness includes the traditional practices, principles, philosophies and beliefs that help you reach a higher reality. They can be the religious, mystical or metaphysical ways that people move outside of their ordinary selves and into a subtler, more sublime and connected reality (the reality of the higher brain). This could include belief and devotion to a God, shamanic rituals, pagan rites, Native American beliefs and ceremonies, Buddhist meditation, Hindu yoga and Eastern practices, New Age beliefs, and even 12-step recovery programs.

We've said in the first chapter that spiritual wellness is geared towards the notions of enlightenment, nirvana, heaven within, cosmic consciousness, paradise on Earth, salvation and grace or Awakening. Sometimes it arrives in a flash of ecstasy with profound insight. Perhaps more often it arrives imperceptibly over time. Even a small taste of the fruits of Awakening can have a profound effect on your life, relieving you of self-torment, stress and suffering, bringing you inner peace and contentment, no matter what happens, and giving you stability, maturity and the fulfillment of wisdom and insight into who you are and how the world works. Just like the other wellnesses, you might put spiritual wellness on your list, not because of what it can lead to, but because the practices in themselves can be fulfilling.

And, to complete the circular chain of wellnesses, spiritual wellness can also unleash the power of the mind and body to heal and help a person recover from incurable diseases. Many physicians and health care professionals know this well. Hospitals and medical schools increasingly offer training in yoga and meditation, and they take into account the religious background of patients in designing treatments. Conversely, physical healing strategies such as fasting and particular diets have had a traditional role in religious experiences.

Any one item or state that you might want out of life is probably in one of these six wellness areas. Together, they make for a full life, each area inexorably linked to the others. To achieve one for very long, it helps to have some degree of all of them at about the same time (see Figure 1).

So what ties the web of wellnesses together? Your brain. There's no physical health without a healthy brain to stimulate your immune system, or happiness without a healthy brain, or the possibility of experiencing love without it. You can't really hope to be fully moral or have passion or spiritual experiences without a fully functioning and healthy brain. What organizes these areas of wellness so that they function at peak levels? An inshifted brain.

An inshifted brain is a brain with its higher areas in charge. An inshifted brain can make the difference between a life of peace, joy and fulfillment and one of bitterness, disappointment and frustration. When your brain is developed many incredible things are possible. It becomes possible to realize your wish list.

That neural inshifting is the center of life makes perfect sense. Managing your senses, body drives and mind to your advantage sends ripples around the wellness wheel, improving your physical health, psychological well-being, relationships, success in society, moral fulfillment and spiritual realization.

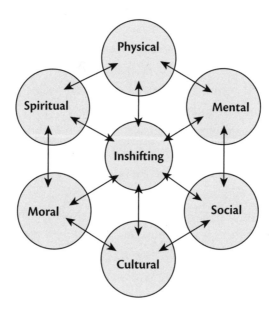

Figure 1. The web of wellnesses

Just as the wellnesses are linked one to another in all directions, a neurally inshifted brain is the critical factor in each. Conversely, all of the wellness areas together—or even alone—can be the catalyst in your successful inshifting.

Now let's explore the brain from the inside out, in the various levels of reality you may experience within a day or at least a lifetime—realities of being "you"!

Part 2

The Realities of You

Men ought to know that from the brain, and from the brain only, arise our pleasures, joys, laughter and jests, as well as our sorrows, pains, griefs and tears. Through it, in particular, we think, see, hear, and distinguish the ugly from the beautiful, the bad from the good, the pleasant from the unpleasant, in some cases using custom as a test, in others perceiving them from their utility. It is the same thing which makes us mad or delirious, inspires us with dread or fear, whether by night or by day, brings sleeplessness, inopportune mistakes, aimless anxieties, absent-mindedness, and acts that are contrary to habit. These things that we suffer all come from the brain, when it is not healthy, but becomes abnormally hot, cold, moist, or dry, or suffers any other unnatural affection to which it was not accustomed. Madness comes from its moistness.

— Hippocrates —

4
Levels of Reality

The brain is the man; its health is essential for normal living; its disorders are surely the most profound of human miseries; and its destruction annihilates a person humanly, however intact his body.

— H. Chandler Elliott —

You are capable of living in different realities. In other words, there are different levels of being "you"! I don't just mean the grouchy "you" and the cheerful "you." I mean there is a lower brain reality "you" that exists on a very different plane than the higher brain reality "you." They are actual or potential aspects of you that experience and interact with the world in substantially different ways.

The lower brain reality is what your senses, body and mind tell you about what is happening inside and around you, and about "who" you are (your identity). Reality, at a higher level, perceives the energy in things and reflects on the process of being aware in each moment, showing you "what" you are and what the universe is. Both are essentially the same. There are also realities that are shades of gray in the middle, many of which you experience every day.

Before we describe a sampling of realities leading up to the highest Awakened reality, it is important to mention that there are many ways to view different levels of reality. For instance, psychologist Abraham Maslow described a hierarchy of needs leading to what he called transcendence (or Awakening). It's a model widely used in the field of psychology and even business motivational seminars.

Maslow's view was that we must satisfy lower, or biological, needs before we satisfy higher psychological and spiritual needs (see Figure 2). When you struggle to meet the biological needs of food, clothing and shelter, your reality can *be* that struggle. If you fear for your own or your family's safety, your reality can *be* there, and there alone, struggling to get safe.

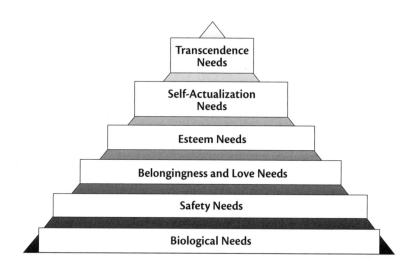

Figure 2. Abraham Maslow's Hierarchy of Needs

Maslow outlined all but one of these levels of needs in his original pyramid, where he originally described self-actualization—authenticity and other positive personality traits—as the highest level. He later realized that transcendence, not self-actualization, was the highest need of humankind.

Transcendence is roughly equivalent to nirvana or enlightenment: for me, these terms are synonymous with Awakening, emphasizing slightly different aspects of the state. For example, Awakening emphasizes the experience of a higher *reality,* enlightenment the *insight,* nirvana the *emotional* peaks, and transcendence the shift beyond one's *personalized viewpoint.* For Maslow, transcendence describes the perspective of transcending ego and normal ways of seeing. As he said in *Religion, Values and Peak-Experiences:* "Man has a higher and transcendent nature, and this is part of his essence, i.e., his biological nature." He described Awakening as "so profound and shaking an experience, that it can change the person's character … forever after." Maslow's theories have become so popular in psychology that they are used by mainstream business to promote employee effectiveness. Thus, the idea of transcendence has become more acceptable to people who would normally consider any idea from Eastern mysticism bizarre.

Although there are many states of reality, here are six representative examples for illustrative purposes. They make all your levels of reality, from the obviously illusory, through the less obvious "ordinary," to the Awakened, more understandable. They are:

- The Dream or Nightmare Reality
- The "Something's Wrong with Your Brain" Reality
- The Daydreaming Reality
- The Willingly Suspended State of Reality
- The Ordinary, Relative World Reality
- The Awakened, Absolute World Reality

5

The Dream or Nightmare Reality

*As a man in his sleep doubts the reality of his
nightmare and yearns to awaken and return to real
life, so the average man of our day cannot, in the depth
of his heart, believe the terrible condition in which
he finds himself—and which is growing worse and
worse—to be a reality. He yearns to attain to a higher
reality, the consciousness of which is already within
him … Our average man has but to make a conscious
effort and ask himself, 'Is not all this an illusion?' in
order to feel like an awakened sleeper, transported from
a hypocritical and horrible nightmare-world into a
living, peaceful, and joyous world of reality.*

— Count Leo Tolstoy —

Remember nights when you were asleep, but trapped in a
nightmare? Your heart pounded with fear as you desperately
strained to escape from something or someone … but couldn't.
Remember nightmares when you were anguished at the thought
of a loved one dying or watching a cherished possession get de-
stroyed? What always happens in the morning? You wake up!

When you're suspended in a nightmare, there eventually
comes a shift. A dawning realization. You feel your body. The
soft mattress. You see your room. The recognition of where you
are. You think, *Wait. Everything's okay. Thank goodness none of that
actually happened. It was only a dream. It wasn't real. Everything is
the way it was. I'm safe.*

It may take a few minutes to recover and for the tension of
the nightmare to subside. That transition is a form of an inshift.

Dreadfulness is gradually replaced by relief and gratitude as you shift from the unreal "reality" of a nightmare to the ordinary "reality" of being awake in your own room. I used nightmares to make the point. Of course, we can also wake from wonderful dreams into harsher realities of life. Either way, the dream-to-waking shift is a transition we all recognize.

What is a higher reality than just being awake? The one you are likely in right now. However, just like the way you view dreams as unreal, you can also view "normal" or everyday states of consciousness as unreal from the vantage point of higher states of reality. Steeped in this typical, ordinary brain reality, you experience it as completely normal—and find it hard to imagine anything higher. But just as there are many states of reality that exist between dreams and "normal" waking, there are states higher than the one you're in now. If you can get to them you would also experience them as more real than the one you're in now!

6

The "Something's Wrong With Your Brain" Reality

*I started to think I was a man of great religious
importance, and to hear voices all the time. I began to
hear something like telephone calls in my head, from
people opposed to my ideas ... The delirium was like a
dream from which I seemed never to awake.*

— *John Forbes Nash* —

The state of "something's wrong with your brain" is the level
of reality that happens when your brain is not functioning
normally. For example, when you're intoxicated your reality is
so altered you are more apt to take unacceptable risks, or when
you take certain drugs you can be deluded and believe plots and
schemes that are not true. Other examples include steroid use
causing rage, being biologically depressed and experiencing everything as hopeless and worthless, and being in a bipolar disorder manic state and spending money because you aren't focused
on consequences. When something is wrong in your brain, you
perceive things differently and behave differently than you would
if your brain were not chemically or electrically out of alignment.

At some point you are likely to experience one of these states
and this level of reality. When your brain is working normally
again you will probably be aghast at how differently you acted
while your brain was out of sorts. Some athletes are aware of how
aggressive they become under the influence of steroids. Some
people know that they get paranoid on marijuana or other illicit
drugs. Many people realize how mistakenly hopeless or irritable
they felt when they were depressed.

Even subtle changes in mood can affect the way you view the world. How often does your mood affect the way you experience life? The drama our brains can construct is like a waking dream. That is why when our brains are under the influence of physical factors—even slight changes in blood sugar—we can experience a downward "shift" in reality, a "sleepening" rather than an Awakening. The shift from one of these states to an ordinary or "normal" state can be as dramatic as shifting from a dream to ordinary reality.

7

The Daydreaming Reality

When ideas float in our mind without any reflection or regard of the understanding, it is that which the French call revery, our language has scarce a name for it.

— *John Locke* —

Sometimes, in a summer morning, having taken my accustomed bath, I sat in my sunny doorway from sunrise till noon, rapt in reverie.

— *Henry David Thoreau* —

While sitting in a boring meeting, class or show, have you ever gone somewhere else? Has your mind wandered to a place where you forget what reality you are in? Haven't you struggled to keep your mind focused in "normal" reality, especially when you are upset about something going on in your life?

Involuntary shifting into a daydream is common. Daydreaming reality is an altered state of reality we all recognize easily. It can happen any time—when you're driving, shopping or eating alone. It's not a true dream reality. And there is nothing "wrong" with your brain at that time. It's just a time when your reality is altered because your mind has taken control of your awareness. It is like being in a trance state.

Many people recall getting fairly involved in a daydream, reliving intense scenes from the past or fantasizing about something. It is possible to get so emotionally involved in a daydream that it can be hard to leave behind. When you are in that daydream, that reality is often more real than what is happening around you. That reality is "you" for those moments.

8

The Willingly Suspended State of Reality

*I think that in theatre you willfully suspend
your disbelief and that you believe that these people
up on the stage are in a castle in Denmark.*

— *Howard Rheingold* —

The willingly suspended state of reality happens when you willingly allow yourself to be consumed by a fantasy. For example, children get so involved in their play that it can become almost as real as their real selves. When you watch a scary movie you can become so caught up in it that your heart pounds or you close your eyes. You know it is just a movie, right, so why are you so affected by it? Some people can become so engrossed by a movie and its characters that they experience an emotional afterglow for hours or days afterward.

That's probably why movies and television shows, particularly soap operas, are so addictive and such a central part of popular culture. They remove people from their ordinary states of reality. Because people want that, we shouldn't underestimate the power of the media and of stories to create dream-like states of reality. People can believe in a well-crafted story and thus feel and act in ways removed from their own judgment and insight.

What we believe, who we think we are, and what we "know" as certain is as malleable as soft clay. As we discussed above, dreams and nightmares, having something wrong with your brain, daydreaming, and willingly suspended states of reality are all levels that illustrate how shiftable our reality is. In the next chapter we'll discuss ordinary, or normal, reality, the one most people live in. This state of being is so "normal" that it is hard to appreciate that it is not the highest level of development and experience that you can reach.

Exercise: Inshifting at the movies

Try taking your first shot at inshifting. Everyone has a child's ability to suspend reality at a moment's notice; everyone has a threshold where they allow themselves to be (or are manipulated into being) immersed in a movie.

What we see can create many kinds of feelings. Sometimes it is enjoyable and sometimes it is not. I don't like the tension when my higher brain allows my mind to get sucked into a suspenseful movie. When I tell myself, "It's just a movie, it's just a movie," this is a form of inshifting. But unless my inshifting skill is up to the challenge of a powerful image I will not be successful. When we tell ourselves "it's just a movie" the brain mechanism that makes that effective is inshifting.

Try this sometime with greater awareness and intention. Inshift at the movies or while watching TV. When you're absorbed in a movie—whether you like it or not—de-identify or disengage your mind so that you pull your attention in from the screen. Be more aware of the whole experience of sitting in the theater or at home at that moment while you're watching the screen. It'll help to relax your body while keeping yourself alert and energized. Experience the movie or TV show as a sensory experience. Make that sensory experience part of the total experience. If you can do that, you know how to inshift!

9

The Ordinary, Relative
World Reality

*The greatest part of mankind ... may be said to be
asleep, and that particular way of life which takes up
each man's mind, thoughts and actions, may be very well
called his particular dream. This particular degree of
vanity is equally visible in every form and order of life.
The learned and the ignorant, the rich and the poor,
are all in the same state of slumber.*

— William Law —

*The highest activities of consciousness have their origins
in physical occurrences of the brain, just as the loveliest
melodies are not too sublime to be expressed by notes.*

— W. Somerset Maugham —

Right now, you know you are not dreaming. Assuming that your brain is working right, you know you're not intoxicated or delusional, and that you aren't lost in a daydream or deliberately acting. So what else is there to wake up from? Is this ordinary and normal "you" the only "you" there is? What could be more real than this ordinary life?

To understand what a higher reality means in practical terms we need a detailed sense of what ordinary reality is. We'll spend some time on this, because you are more likely to experience an intentional inshift into an Awakened world reality if you fully understand your ordinary reality that is as invisible to you as water is to a fish. But first let's review all the states of reality from the perspective of the brain (keeping in mind that we'll go into more detail in Part 3).

The Brain and Reality Levels

All six levels of reality are created by the interplay of your lower and higher brain. Lower brain areas are most activated when we dream. That's where your higher brain has the *least* control and is least activated. In the higher rungs of reality, the Awakened ones, your higher brain areas are in control, and in fact, everything is recognized as being a product of the workings of your own brain. Ordinary reality lies between dreaming and full Awakening. Until the brain is fully Awakened, all reality appears to comes from what Albert Einstein called "the optical illusion of consciousness."

Ordinary reality, then, is where both lower and higher brain areas are activated, but the lower brain remains in greater control. What does that mean, to have your higher brain activated with awareness on some level, but to have your lower brain in control? It means that in ordinary reality you are most likely only faintly in touch with the ultimate fact and only thing you can truly know, which is that you are alive in this unique moment. Conversely, the lower your level of reality, the more your attention is focused on the *contents* of your SBMA. There's no awareness of the process of awareness, no awareness that your brain is being aware. It's like being immersed in a movie, without the ability to know you are watching a movie. In this case, the movie is produced by the programming of your SBMA.

Believe it or not, ordinary reality encompasses a broad range of experience and behavior, from suicide bombers to teenagers who identify with a clique to the average person obsessed by getting ahead in the world. For instance, most of us play roles in life: mature adult, cool dude, sweet female, respected professional, doting grandmother. For many of us, and probably for most of us, we are so ingrained in these roles that even though we may know intellectually there is more to us, we have a hard time acting otherwise, such as a grandmother who has a hard time seeing herself dance at a rock concert or a cool dude who finds it disconcerting to enjoy playing cards with a group of older folks.

There are other things besides roles that you have learned to believe, things that are harder to see. For example, right now you probably believe you are an unchanging person, a consistent self making your way through life. Yet, nothing is the same about you, all of the chemicals that make up your body periodically change completely. Even your memory that bridges the past with the future is altered over time.

In particular, your senses are also not what they seem. Here's an example: you most likely believe you are looking at things around you. Yet, what you can *see* around you right now, the light from all the objects you're looking at, enters your eyes, hits the back of your retinas and is transformed into neurons that relay chemical messages. Then the neurons that relay chemical messages stimulate other neurons that change them into patterns of nerve pulses. These are conducted in an intricate code to the back of your brain where the visual areas are.

So, then, what do you actually "see"? There is no light in your head: it's dark in there! What you are "seeing" is a decoding of those patterns of nerve impulses. Essentially, you're reading the brain's Morse code. It's not direct reality. It's a representation.

The same holds for what you think and believe. Most people believe that their lives and their actions come from their conscious choosing, not their programming. By doubting these aspects of reality, "standing back" so to speak and witnessing the fact of your SBMA's programming, you can inshift into a higher reality.

The Mind and Ordinary Reality

Remember, the mind and the other aspects of your lower brain are *tools* of your brain. In particular, your mind is software—vital software—that resides in lower brain areas. It's a shorthand way to process and screen enormous amounts of information by constructing categories and stories, plots and scripts. Every moment of your life can be classified and stored in your brain, billions of sensory inputs that help make thousands of decisions and actions every second.

That is why your mind constructs images and scenes from outside in the world, even from its memory, just like in your dreams. It sums up your experience by explaining it to you. If you walk into a room and scan it, the billions of bits of information from your senses would overwhelm you if your mind didn't sum it all up in concepts such as "a tree," "my uncle's room" and "the air is chilly." So, your mind actually constructs a reality for you.

For example, the stimulus patterns that form an inkblot, but which look like clouds in the sky, are just your mind assimilating these patterns into known categories. Your reality is built from the simplest categories to the more complex. For example, say you view a random inkblot and see it as "a chicken." That image can become a story, like "the chicken is crossing the road." In that way all of your realities to this point are created and reinforced. So, the more you perceive that inkblot as a chicken, the harder it is to see it any other way. That is how we get stuck in our programmed realities. That's how most of humanity gets trapped in an ordinary reality.

Then, for extra good measure, your reality is communicated by that constant narrator inside your head that describes everything to you. This is also how your mind creates part of your reality.

The deepest part of that mind-constructed reality is an "I" or "self." It is the earliest and most deeply ingrained category and story your mind uses to explain the world. And every experience reinforces it. The "I" or "self," also called an "ego," is the reference point for the mind-programming that tells you the story of "you," that you are a consistent person, a separate person, making your way through life. That "ego" function of your mind is the ultimate shorthand for knowing how to literally get around in the world. It is the shorthand for being able to do *anything* that requires self-representation, such as knowing how to refer to yourself in a conversation. It's a critical piece of fiction—extremely valuable, but a fiction nonetheless. It's a model, not a real experience of how things are. It's not nearly the highest reality you can know. In fact, your mind's egocentric or self-centric slant is so strong that it is the factor that keeps you in an ordinary reality, the main barrier to keeping you from realizing a higher reality.

Experiencing that slant is key to inshifting and Awakening. By believing in the model of reality that has you starring in your ordinary life reality—your waking "dream"—you aren't likely to question any other aspects of your mind. That's because your mind uses your ego to shape everything! It explains everything, literally telling you how to get from here to there. Your "I" is used by your mind for self-referenced explanations of what is happening to and around you. Your constant narrator represents that "I," telling you who you are and why the world is the way it is. Again, this illusion of an "I" makes it harder to experience the illusion of your ordinary reality.

What are some of the forces of your mind that keep you stuck in a self-created ordinary world?

One is the addiction to finding future pleasure. That has you packing more things into each hour, the need to urgently get everything done. Urgency (which creates an adrenalin addiction in itself) comes from other people's programming. Society, school, family, church and corporate advertising all push you to want to cram as much pleasure into your life and avoid as much discomfort as you can. The result is that you sacrifice the bliss of being alive in each moment.

Not all pleasure is hedonistic and blocks the enjoyment of being alive. Some pleasure is "spiritual" and comes from self-sacrificing. However, if it isn't driven inside, by your conscious choice, and if it doesn't help you inshift, you are apt to be a pleasure-driven, discomfort-phobic automaton. Your ordinary reality is sustained by being on conditioned autopilot, but if you had a broader perspective, much of the urgency would disappear.

What's abnormal about being programmed early in child-hood? What if you like the values and role you've been given? What's wrong with getting pleasure and avoiding pain? Isn't it normal to have a programmable mind, a reactive body and set interpretations of life events? Doesn't an ordinary reality include paying your bills, living within a budget so you can retire earlier and maintaining your home?

There is nothing wrong with having values, attitudes and am-bitions instilled in childhood. There's nothing wrong with want-ing to get ahead, have financial security, provide for your future, protect your children, safeguard your health, and live as long as you can with as much pleasure and least discomfort as possible. Here is the problem: in the ordinary reality, it is easy to get stuck in programmed values, beliefs and desires, in things instilled in you by the world instead of discovered as you get deeply in touch with what is profoundly important to you.

Why do we get stuck in this level of reality, in this stage of development, so that we keep values that don't serve our deepest desires for happiness and peace? Why do we allow immediate attractions and aversions to control us and become obsessions? Because we mistake having pleasure and avoiding discomfort for inner happiness and peace. Because we get fooled into believing that ordinary reality is absolute reality, that our experience of the world and of what is good and bad for us must be right. We don't know any different, because we don't run across many people who live in higher reality.

You can get unconsciously programmed to believe that there is a perfect life and an ideal way to live it, that getting respect, being admired and acquiring wealth feel good and always equate with inner happiness. That is why ordinary reality leads to exis-tential unhappiness: a sense of meaninglessness, emptiness and boredom that can't be filled. Without context, without continual inshifting to a higher reality, your ordinary reality becomes stagnant, an unfulfilled dream, if not a nightmare.

Being stuck in an ordinary reality, what seem to be innocent, healthy and ordinary aims, such as being financially organized or guarding your health, can get derailed and become obsessions over things like fame and fortune or aging. It can wear you down to an early death. And even if you stick with laudable goals and achieve financial comfort or reasonable health and well-being, what good are they if you become dissatisfied and miss an opportunity for the most profound experiences you are capable of?

You have to guard against complacency in your ordinary realities. You have to make sure that you take the time to learn about yourself (and inshift in the process) without getting caught in the allures of an ordinary reality: promotions at work, doing things to be admired or accepting a less than fulfilling life. Keep in mind that we are not talking about an occasional indulgence but an obsession that can ruin a life.

Remember, the elements of your lower brain (your senses, body, mind and automatic actions, or SBMA) meld together through its automatic systems to create an ordinary waking reality. The force of that reality is *extremely* difficult to resist: it is almost impossible to stop thinking or feeling or to suppress your drives and reinterpret the life events that everyone else believes, too. It takes some deftness to inshift by detaching from those things (not stopping them, detaching from them) while they are going on.

As you'll discover, having context is a major part of an Awakened reality—that is, not getting locked into a particular focus. Think about what a challenge it is to have context, to be fully present when you urgently have to urinate! Try being more fully aware that you are alive when your child is in danger. How difficult is it to realize the miracle of your aliveness when you are in pain? We all know what it's like to keep perspective when you feel irritable and out of sorts. Ordinary people who are mature—

maybe not Awakened, but emotionally more grown-up—do hang on to a wider and broader view of difficult moments all the time. Some are better at it than others, and at different times. Yogis and deeply religious people have described aspects of inshifting techniques for thousands of years.

A Consensus Trance

Is it just a matter of not inshifting enough that keeps us trapped in an ordinary reality?

Yes, although human culture conspires to challenge inshifting with what philosopher and psychologist George Gurjieff calls a consensus trance. Gurjieff believed that the vast majority of people live in a hypnotic-like trance, where your higher brain is induced to be less active than normal. It is a trance where you are more passive and gullible, susceptible to the powerful conditioning of society.

For example, the sight of delectable French fries might entice you to go to a fast food restaurant, because you saw them eaten on a television commercial. That deliberate manipulation of your reality traps you further inside the consensus trance of an ordinary reality. Or you might consider yourself a loser and unworthy of love because of an idea instilled in your childhood and continually reinforced by a critical society. Inshifting is a way to make your higher brain *more* functional; ordinary reality is perpetuated by a less than fully functional higher brain.

A consensus trance is similar to a hypnotic trance, except you don't need to relax and focus on a swinging watch. It is a state of hyper-suggestibility in which select thoughts and feelings are more easily and powerfully triggered by suggestions made by society around you. Suggestions are purposeful or even unintentional words or images that cause you to think, feel, believe and act in certain ways. They are expressed by people in authority who want to influence you, by media images, or by your peers; they are whatever programs and influences your mind. These suggestions can create their effect so subtly, quickly and automatically that you will believe it was your idea. You will believe you made a fully conscious decision to think or do something. The point here is that, settled into your ordinary reality, you will believe that you are autonomous and self-directed. But that's because you have no idea that almost every aspect of "you" is programmed. And that a higher reality awaits where you freshly create yourself every moment.

For instance, a hypnotist can purposefully say words that persuade you to quit smoking or believe you're a good person. When you're in a consensus trance it is the suggestions of your culture—parents, friends, billboards, commercials, work associates—that shape who you are without you fully knowing how much influence these forces have over you. They make you believe, for example, that you need to fit in, have more stuff or believe youth equals happiness.

The conditions of a consensus trance begin to be formed in childhood. By the time you are an adult, you are deeply rooted in an ordinary reality. By that time almost everyone absolutely believes that they and the world are a certain way. For example, an ordinary reality is so foundational that if your parents responded quickly to your cries as a baby, you would likely be programmed to believe that the world is a responsive place and things should immediately go your way.

Many attitudes were implanted in your mind with these powerfully encoded schemata (or associations in your mind), including how much power and presence you believe you have, how lovable and worthy you believe you are, whether the world is a welcoming or hostile place or whether it is right to be optimistic or pessimistic. Hundreds of attitudes and beliefs like that, whether straightforward, in mixed messages, or in contradictory ideas, were planted in your mind, to be triggered throughout your life. Most of these you take for granted and never question.

Those core assumptions about yourself and life are at the

core of an ordinary reality, of an ordinary you. They create fertile ground for a deepening consensus trance in which your ordinary reality becomes invisible and is continually reinforced as your mind screens out things which don't confirm its programmed reality.

If you don't stimulate your higher brain and break your trance by learning to inshift you'll always be susceptible to undue influence. The scariest influence comes from the multi-billion-dollar advertising industry, which employs psychologists and advertising personnel to figure out how to deepen your consensus trance to influence your buying behavior. Their job can be an honorable and necessary part of an honest company trying to sell things, but it is also to create artificial needs: anything that you don't really need, like fancy cars and fashionable clothes.

Even the basic things you do need can be packaged in creative and expensive ways. Subconscious messages are a technique to induce trances in movies, showing branded products used by popular actors, to make you more likely to want those products. Even the popular media in general, as part of the creative process, implant in you a version of ideal: they tell you what is cool and normal, how normal and abnormal people feel and think. A fundamental trap in a consensus trance is that the more things are implanted in us, the more suggestible we are. It snowballs! We can become what one author called "a nation of sheep."

In a consensus trance we become stuck in the relative world. It's a similar but perhaps not as intense state as a full hypnotic trance. Just like dreams and nightmares, in a consensus trance the plots and scripts of our lives are largely implanted in us or suggested to us by society and the people in our early lives. We are programmed to be who we are, to be our roles in society, to believe what we *should* value and want out of life. Popular movies, commercials and television programs cause you to want to lead an ideal life. That includes having an ideal family, the ideal body, the ideal emotions. Even when you see flawed characters on screen as rebels or thieves, somehow people idealize them and want to be them.

The more programmed we are the harder it is for us to be de-programmed, and the more difficult it is for us to experience our-selves and the world any other way. Just like seeing the chicken in the inkblot, the more we see it that way the harder it is to see it any other way. We become trapped in our consensus trance. We believe what we are trained to believe, experience how we are conditioned to experience, act and react according to pro-grammed identities instead of by true choice. Our expectations, our self-esteem, our roles in life, our relationships, even our reli-gious beliefs can be determined more by the forces of society and upbringing than by free spontaneous choice or self-awareness. That's the relative ordinary world that most of us live in.

It's inevitable and necessary that you are programmed to some degree. Yet, most people are fully entranced by the time they reach adulthood. Breaking your consensus trance and Awaken-ing from your ordinary reality is a normal progression of human development that practically no one fulfills to their highest pos-sible levels.

"Not me," you say. "I am fully just me, in control of my life. I have decided who I am and what I believe, and I'm probably as Awakened as I can be or as much as I want to be."

So how do you know you are fixed into an ordinary reality, so you can see more clearly? Think how many times you have felt stuck in your habits and usual ways of seeing events and people, when you wanted to break free of the normal ways of being you so you could be spontaneous, totally yourself, able to laugh and sing when you wanted, dance unselfconsciously or immediately speak up when you disagree with someone. Set in your ordinary reality, you are usually controlled by your emotions and drives to, say, buy things or eat to feel good, envy people you feel are luckier than you, feel sorry for yourself, or become irritable and frustrated when things don't go your way. If you have sabotaged yourself by being angry when you wanted to be loving, jealous when you wanted to be at peace, cruel when you wanted to be kind, you are steeped in an ordinary reality. It's also when you playact at work or in social settings you aren't familiar with by, for example, trying to act more relaxed, confident or happy than you really are, or behaving the way you think an adult should, so no one thinks you're weird, different or messed up.

Are you sure you know who you really are?

In the consensus trance of an ordinary reality you are controlled by what society thinks of you. Do you narrowly follow fashion trends? Is your hair style much different that the norm? True, sometimes you have to play the game to accomplish what you want in life, but how much is the game playing you? We are a tribal species and each of us wants to belong, but how much have you bought into society's expectations of you? That's your consensus trance, your ordinary reality.

In your ordinary normal reality you easily and often over-personalize events and people's actions. You overreact to something you think is a slight when it isn't. We've all done it. That's why I call it ordinary. Have you jumped to a conclusion and made accusations with scant evidence? Have you filled in wide gaps of a story to complete the picture? That's the effect of your consensus trance. To insist that the world is fair to you, that success always comes if you try hard enough, to become irate in heavy traffic—all these are part of a consensus trance. (Hopefully, you were able to realize later how irrational it was to take traffic personally—as if it existed just to block you!)

Without some way to counter the trance, to lift yourself out of your ordinary reality, your human mind remains extremely impressionable and suggestible, often even superstitious and gullible. That can't go well. Just like the way wonderful dreams can become nightmares if we stay in them too long, just like a drug high often "crashes" into a miserable aftereffect, and just like we would get sick of living in the perfect world of a Hollywood movie, the ordinary state of reality eventually turns sour if there is nothing to balance it. We become frustrated when things don't go our way and then get attached to whatever does. Even the person with the most secure identity and clear life goals eventually becomes blocked to real happiness without continually developing and learning to inshift.

Again, the relative world is practical and necessary to our lives. There is nothing inherently bad or wrong with it. And there's nothing wrong with our minds being programmed to succeed. It's a great thing to be able to pay bills, drive a car, and keep your life organized and predictable. It is good to make yourself successful and admired by others, to find love and affection. You just don't want to get *stuck* in the relative world of the mind without the balance of the absolute world of the higher brain. When you are stuck that way, in that level of reality, you don't know there are any higher levels.

Getting trapped in an ordinary reality is so much easier these days because you can achieve things so much easier with modern technology than ever before. The easier things are to achieve the busier we get with each passing generation. The more we can think of to do, the more we can achieve, the more we try to do. You can drive and speak to anyone around the world you want at the same time. We have become obsessed with achieving and addicted to doing. That makes your ordinary reality a much more powerful trap.

Your Death and Ordinary Reality

Let's get down to the basement of an ordinary reality. This last aspect of ordinary reality is perhaps the most strangely problematic. It is this: because it uses, organizes itself around, and clings to the paradigm of an "I," your mind automatically denies, minimizes or avoids the certainty of its own death. It makes sense, really. To bolster an image of a self that is central to the universe your mind must experience that it cannot end. To no longer exist is as inconceivable to your mind as the idea of infinity. It's fearful and painful. Of course we all realize on an intellectual level that we are going to die, it is just that denial makes us not emotionally believe it. We live like we are never going to get old, breathe our last breath and close our eyes for the last time. Or we can deny life by deferring to a belief that we are going to live on as a spirit or that we are going to know that we are dead after we are dead, regardless of whether those beliefs are true or not.

Denial of our own death can be a good thing. It can keep us from the hopeless despair and fear that the thought of our death can bring. Staving off the bitter reality that we will lose everything we cherish and everyone we love, including ourselves, denial helps us hope that there are always possibilities. Denying, pretending or convincing ourselves that we are going to live forever can keep us productively focused on the future.

Yet denial can keep us prisoner. It lies at the heart of your ordinary reality because it makes it easier for you to avoid facing your fears. All of our main fears come down to an ultimate fear of annihilation: if we can't face our own death we can't face any of our deepest fears, whether of heights, the dark, monsters, being alone, loss of control, or going crazy. That's because they all lead to the fear of losing ourselves. Wanting to survive forever, our mind is susceptible to the trance-like programming that creates the ordinary reality and easily induces us to believe things instead of stopping to think long enough to feel nothingness. It keeps us, our SBMA, able to blot out the reality of our own mortality with constant drama, beliefs and drives.

Denying our own death makes us feel increasingly anxious and unsettled, if even at a low grade. We know on a deeper level what the truth is. It takes energy to keep from feeling it. That anxiety (called existential angst) is an emotional state that usually gets worse as we reach middle age. When that happens, many people become even more focused on looking and acting young: think of the cliché of middle-aged men buying red sports cars

and the booming field of anti-aging cosmetic surgery and therapies.

Denying mortality is perhaps the cruelest consequence of an
overactive mind not balanced by the higher brain, because denying our own death keeps us numb to the miracle of being alive.
It prevents us from cherishing each moment of our lives. That
profound appreciation is one of the essential elements of what it
means to Awaken to the absolute world within us.

So what would a world look like to someone who lived not
in an ordinary normal reality but in an Awakened reality? What
does it mean to Awaken from an ordinary reality? Before we tack-
le these questions, here's a fairy tale that may illustrate the process
of self realization, of shifting up.

Two Worlds Found in a Tail: A Fairy Tale

*Once upon a time, in the thick, soupy oceans of planet Earth, a living
cell was created. It was the first step of a brilliant universal blueprint
that called the cell to change, grow and evolve over time.*

*Those early days were difficult for this simple cell. Floating in the
primordial soup, with only his simple membrane to protect him, he
was subject to cold, volcanic heat, acid rains and salt flows. The poor
little cell, shriveled by salt and scorched by acids, suffered his surroundings until his membrane thickened and he grew little portals of entry
and exit, allowing him to control what chemicals came in and out and
how he reacted to the environment. He learned how to soak up the
chemicals he needed for survival and to close up his membrane portals
for resistance against caustic environments. Eventually, he was able to
shrivel his membrane on one side so he could slowly writhe his way
through the soup to avoid the caustic tides. Even though he was often
ineffective, what a glorious time it was for the little cell!*

*Things went fairly well for this little entity, except that the cur-
rents of his soupy ocean environment grew stronger. He found it harder
to fight these currents, despite writhing with all his might. He didn't*

know that he had grown a tail to help him easily and quickly glide through his liquid world; he didn't stop his desperate struggle long enough to realize it!

He thought the way he functioned was the best and only way. He didn't know there was another way to be. All he saw around him were his fellow cells twisting and squirming like he was, until the day he saw another cell easily scooting around, proudly swishing his tail, merrily swimming.

Suddenly, awareness came to the little cell; he felt the presence of his own tail! He would no longer have to struggle to avoid harsh environments. Peace and contentment rushed in—a superior feeling. He felt even better than he did when he learned to control his inner world.

Although it took some time to master, he eventually learned to easily glide through the soupy water, waking as many of his comrades to the freedom of their tails as he could.

The fairy tale is our human story. In the beginning of our lives we are controlled by the circumstances and reality thrust upon us. As we develop, when life inevitably leads to at least some turmoil and suffering, we are trained and hypnotized into dealing with life according to the rules of a consensus trance created by society. That trance builds on our basic instincts and neural makeup to induce us to meet our needs in a way that conforms to society's needs first: we want to be happier and fulfilled, so we look outward. We project into the world our interpretation. Our own waking trance perpetuates this projection, inducing in us a survival mode mentality that has us look for external means of gratification. In the process we don't realize that within us—not in the world, but *within us*—is the ultimate means to happiness. But how do we find this potential? *Where* is it inside us?

10

The Awakened, Absolute
World Reality

*The ordinary sense of things around me faded.
For the moment nothing but an ineffable joy and
exaltation remained. It is impossible to fully describe the
experience. It was like the effect of some great orchestra
when all the separate notes have melted into one swelling
harmony that leaves the listener conscious of nothing
save that his soul is being wafted upward, and almost
bursting with its own emotion.*

— *Anonymous Christian clergyman* —

One of the foundations of physics is the second law of thermodynamics. That law describes a process called entropy. Entropy means that everything in the universe is moving towards complete disorganization and chaos. Eventually everything in the universe will decay and disintegrate so even heat will dissipate into cold black nothingness.

Against the force of entropy is a lesser force that creates, just like how organized eddies form in a sea of splashing random water. Spectacular twists and impossible events created the entity that *knows it is reading this*. Against the powerful force of entropy is the momentum that converted energy into matter and that congealed matter into stars and planets, including one rare planet that existed at the right distance from its star to create life. That planet had to have an enormous amount of a unique and remarkable substance called water, and the right carbon-based organic molecules that eventually evolved into cells that could replicate with DNA and, with countless trillions of accidents, developed into bacteria, insects, birds, antelopes, tigers, apes and humans.

Now, consider this: after all that, one sperm out of billions reached one particular egg and made you! It doesn't matter whether you believe this all resulted from the conscious choice of a God, by virtue of intelligent, natural laws, or complete randomness over long periods of time, the point is exactly the same. You are unbelievably lucky to have made it to be you, the conscious human that you are. You beat the astronomical odds against your being here, odds much greater than being able to randomly pick one particular grain of sand out of all the grains of sand in all the oceans and beaches of the world. You won the universal lottery. You were born and are here, alive, aware, right now!

If you were to grasp even a sliver of the magnitude of what that means, that you are alive right now, you would Awaken to a higher reality and your life would be completely transformed. That realization would rearrange your values and priorities, whatever your troubles. You would understand the extreme good fortune that is your existence and cherish each moment of your life, regardless. Gratitude for making it to existence as a conscious being would well up as you developed a kindred bond with everything and everyone that came into existence along with you. It leaves an unshakable inner peace and joy, an inner contentment that is deeper than the happiness that comes from fleeting, temporary pleasures.

And so learning to inshift means that you are actually learning, among other things, to Awaken. Awakening begins where the fifth step of inshifting leaves off—with an acute realization of your aliveness right now. I call that a ROYAL Now (Realization of Your Aliveness). When you can value and cherish your existence, even the existence of other people, animals and material things so that you feel privileged—like royalty—that is an aspect of Awakening. In an absolute sense you are already successful. You were born successful because you are here and experiencing now. That you exist is a miraculous expression of a universal intelligence. You are royally lucky to be able to channel that intelligence.

Awakening is also many other things, including an experience of connectedness.

The morning I wrote this I was sitting outside at a table eating a sandwich. Several little birds landed on the table, looking for crumbs. As I looked at the birds I drew my attention inward and could witness more of the totality of the moment. It dawned on me how remarkable it is that cities are so totally dominated by humans but that there are scores of wild animals who claim this equally as their home. Insects, birds, squirrels and mice share the city and the world with us. It is *our* planet. I felt connected to these little creatures. I felt like a part of their world, instead of just seeing them in mine. I was grateful that there are still wild animals, that we had not extinguished wildlife in favor of stocked fish and domesticated pets.

That was a tiny epiphany, a sliver of an Awakening. Most people have minute epiphanies like that. As you spend more time inshifting, epiphanies happen more frequently, intensely and unexpectedly. For instance, once while I was driving I came to a four-way intersection as three other drivers approached. Each waited for the others' signal to move. We determined the order we would cross the intersection in seconds. We all knew what to do and executed our maneuvers smoothly and efficiently, like being in a choreographed dance. I felt a moment of joy being part of the traffic, something bigger than myself. It was a giddy, profound feeling, being interconnected with the other drivers, all of us bound by the collective rules we all knew and followed.

In Charles Dickens' *A Christmas Carol*, Ebenezer Scrooge, a once bitter and miserly old man, is awakened from sleep and Awakened from his embittered mind. The ghosts of Christmas Past, Present and Future gave him the detached higher perspective he needed to find freedom and happiness and connectedness to friends and community. He overcame his entrenched beliefs and attitudes and began valuing relationships over money. Every moment of his life became precious.

As we briefly touched on in the last chapter, Awakening is also the experience of context.

Context is circumstance, background, the larger picture, the surrounding perspective. What is the deepest context you can experience? It is the experience of your existence each moment. Context comes from reflective awareness—your ability to know that you know. It tells you that the moment is happening. That's the deepest context.

If you can experience that degree of context you'll find out that perceiving the world with you at the epicenter is not the only way to see the world. It's not be-all and end-all reality. That all-pervasive context where you are acutely aware of being alive in each moment melts away the experience that everything that is happening is about you. It helps relieve you of the burden of obsessively screening everything for what it can get you, for whether it will cause you to feel good or bad. It softens the relentless fight to prove your ego-self is worthy of respect and love, to prove to yourself that it will live indefinitely. Not experiencing everything from the perspective of your ego-self is the crux of an Awakened reality—the reality equated with the highest degree of mental well-being, the highest level of mental health.

Of course, an Awakened reality doesn't mean to give up on that function of your mind. You certainly want to know what you should move towards or away from. It's just that perspective gives you more control of your momentary drives and impulses. It lets you let go of wanting, craving, fearing and avoiding, in favor of experiencing the wonder and import of each moment. It's just not necessary to scan every waking second for what it can get you, for things that may upset you, or to explain every moment.

Context is one aspect of an Awakened reality that helps snap you out of the mentality that life and each event that makes it up has a plot that must have a happy ending. "Happy endings" happen continually when you appreciate the perfection of your existence.

Recognizing context of any kind means that, to some extent, you have inshifted. If, for example, you interpret that someone is being rude to you, even a basic level of perspective will allow you to see that it has actually nothing to do with you and everything to do with them as a frail human projecting their own emotional turmoil on you. That perspective can offset stress and move you further towards this highest level of being you! When you experience the widest context—your aliveness each now—an inner joy, a deeper peace and a mature wisdom pervade even in the face of hardship, discomfort, pleasure and excitement.

In an Awakened reality, the foreground becomes context. The elements of your relative world slip into the background. Your entire mind's categories and stories, your body's sensations, urges and reactions, even your perceptions of your senses, events, objects and body sensations become a unified backdrop that contribute to context and your ultimate Awakening.

Awakening: Fact or Fiction?

If you think that Awakening is more myth than fact you're not alone. Many people don't believe an Awakening is real. That is because being Awakened is hard to relate to and tricky to comprehend. Most people are not even close to Awakened. Yet Awakenings have been documented since the beginnings of human civilization, and in every generation, from all walks of life, both religious and secular. These Awakened people have discovered the astounding potential within their own brain, an inner gift described as extraordinary, beyond words, life altering.

One thing is very clear about Awakening. If you read beyond the fantastic, other-worldly and metaphorical descriptions in religious and secular writings, you understand Awakening as what ought to be a normal stage of human development. To that end, having some degree of Awakening, some insight that removes you from your ordinary mind, is not a luxury. The highest stages of human development are just the fulfillment of your maturity as an adult as you leave the reality of your mind. Your mind is a program set up for uneasiness, unfulfillment, inner conflict, anxiety, grief, struggle, and even dire unhappiness and self-destructiveness. Reaching to meet your highest needs and fullest potential of your brain helps you fulfill your lower and higher needs. It corrects the dysfunction inherent in your brain's mind.

To approach Awakening is to approach a cure for *your* human "condition." (Yes, *your* condition, even if you believe you are just fine.) The more Awakened you are the more of an antidote you have to Buddha's axiom: "Life is suffering." It is the epitome of mental health, of what it means to live a meaningful life not bound to resentment, bitterness, fear, anxiety, sadness or grief. Neural inshifting is the only vehicle that can take you down that road, no matter what you call it or how it is accomplished.

How can Awakening be relevant to your life when you have more immediate concerns, including health, finances, children or time? Continually Awakening your brain through inshifting is infinitely practical precisely because it enhances physical healing and fosters vibrant health, psychological maturity, deep and loving social connections, competence in daily living, the creation of a fulfilling purpose and values-driven life, and a sacred appreciation for the interconnectedness of things exactly as they are.

Awakening Your Brain

As you learn all the steps of neural inshifting, you come to a level of reflective awareness where you see what you really are as a process that can experience. You transcend ego and experience not as an "I" but as an "it."

You realize that reality, like waves and water, is both the perception of sensations (energy vibrations) coming from your SBMA and the representation of your SBMA as information. Information being, for example, what you experience as "things," "events," "time," "people," or the identity of "you." Implied in that double perception is a subtle and sublime reality: everything is ultimately energy in one form or another, even you!

So the epiphanies of Awakening are that you are a process, not a "me," and that reality is both energy and an interpretation of the information in your SBMA. And when the information value perceived by your lower brain abruptly moves into the background, even for an instant, you and everything else are experienced as universal connectedness. That super-epiphany is part of an Awakening.

Other aspects of an Awakening are, as we've said, the experience of context or perspective as well as wonder or a radical amazement in your existence, and an ecstasy that rivals a drug high. It's been reported to be a life-altering experience.

In the language of behavioral science, Roger Walsh summarized an Awakening as having five parts: "(1) ineffability: the experience is of such power and so different from ordinary experience as to give the sense of defying description, (2) noesis: a heightened sense of clarity and understanding, (3) altered perception of space and time, (4) appreciation of the holistic, unified, integrated nature of the universe and one's unity with it, (5) intense positive affect, including a sense of the perfection of the universe." (Walsh, 1980)

In religious terms, the Judeo-Christian bible states: "Be in the world, but not of the world." As you Awaken from a consensus trance, you must still be in the game of life, but you can also experience the novelty, strangeness and miracle of a higher reality and a deeper outlook on life.

Yet, even though Awakening seems fantastic and otherworldly, it really is only a process of more completely accessing your higher brain areas. It's a stage of development, the highest level of maturity, the epitome of mental health. As you learn the five steps of neural inshifting you will see Awakening as Steps 6 and higher. (Which is the value of neural inshifting, in that it takes you right up to the door of an Awakening.) Of course, when you more fully experience it, Awakening becomes normal, life fulfillment feels normal: wonderful, but normal.

11

The Road to Awakening

Man stands in strict connection with a higher fact
never yet manifested. There is power over us and behind
us, and we are channels of its communications.

— *Ralph Waldo Emerson* —

There is a Zen saying roughly translated as "Cross the river with every step." As you live fully in each moment, no past or future, every step you take to inshift, you Awaken yourself. No matter where you are in your inshifting ability, no matter what step you are learning or whether you are learning its essence as a complete skill, you cross to the other shore with every step, every step in essence being complete in itself.

Life doesn't wait until you reach the other side, it's not just a means to an end. In that sense, Awakening is living life to its fullest, no matter what is happening, because you are immersed in each moment. It's not a destination, a way to be someone or something else. Roshi (Zen Master) Shunryu Suzuki likens a gradual, imperceptible Awakening to being "drenched walking in mist."

As you practice inshifting, Awakening little-by-little, you transcend your ordinary self a bit every moment. There may be points where there are small epiphanies or a dramatic Awakening experience, as we'll see. These more spectacular moments don't just happen to a brain that isn't at least somewhat prepared for it. That is, you can prepare for Awakenings deliberately, by inshifting, or by whatever helps you grow in maturity and wisdom, but once any mark of development happens, it must be cultivated. You don't just become a great baseball player and then stop training. Lasting insights and lasting skills of neural inshifting need to be nurtured. There is no static or permanently Awakened state.

There are two broad ways to Awaken: the sudden, accidental inshift and the gradual, purposeful inshift that happens with deliberate training. Both ways are usually involved.

The Accidental Path

Think about the horror of terminal illness or of a parent who has just lost a child and you'll understand the depths of despair. The accidental path to Awakening happens when your programmed mind is driven past the point of overload. Attached to its ordinary, conditioned world your mind experiences some extreme event that tears apart that attachment and reaches a crisis. Your mind's ordinary coping strategies stop working and your rational mind shuts down. Beyond meaning, future, blame or solace in victimhood, your mind loses its grip on your attention. Rules and ideas don't work, the hold on emotions often slips, feelings careen out of control, nothing makes sense, the mind cannot do its stabilizing job, nothing in its conditioning brings order ... and ordinary reality dissolves.

There are two main outcomes: either you shut down and fall into crisis and experience a mental breakdown, psychiatric symptoms, physical illness or even suicide, or the higher brain takes over from the lower and a transcendent inshift happens.

Here are some extraordinary examples of accidental Awakenings that will illustrate what a strong Awakening is like. Remember, most Awakenings happen in microscopic increments along a long path of inshifting practice.

The first example is from Bill W, one of the founders of Alcoholics Anonymous. After repeated hospitalizations for drunken binges, he woke up one day to a new experience:

> Suddenly the room lit up with a great white light. I was
> caught up into an ecstasy which there are no words to

describe. It seemed to me, in the mind's eye that I was on a mountain and that a wind not of air but of spirit was blowing. And it was burst upon me that I was a free man. Slowly the ecstasy subsided. I lay on the bed, but now for a time I thought I was in another world, a new world of consciousness. All about me and through me there was a wonderful feeling of Presence and I thought to myself, "So this is the God of the preachers!" A great peace stole over me and I thought, "No matter how wrong things seem to be, they are still alright. Things are all right with God and His world." (Anonymous, 12 Step literature)

No biochemical-induced euphoria, Bill W's insight was a re-action to the severe psychological condition he found himself in. He didn't meditate or practice neural-wellness inshifting. It happened to him. He was fortunate enough to be able to draw on whatever inner strength he had.

Another example of an incredible Awakening happened to author Eckhart Tolle during a state of dire depression, as recounted in his book, *The Power of Now* (New World Library, 1997).

I woke up ... with a feeling of absolute dread ... more intense than it had ever been.... The most loathsome thing of all, however, was my own existence.

"I cannot live with myself any longer." This was the thought that kept repeating itself in my mind. Then suddenly I became aware of what a peculiar thought it was. "Am I one or two? If I cannot live with myself there must be two of me: the 'I' and the 'self' that I cannot live with." "Maybe," I thought, "only one of them is real." I was so stunned by this strange realization that my mind stopped. I was fully conscious, but there were no more thoughts. Then I felt drawn into what seemed like a vortex of energy. It was a slow movement at first and then accelerated. I was gripped by an intense fear, and my body started to shake. I heard the words "resist nothing," as if spoken inside my chest. I could feel myself being sucked into a void. It felt as if the void were inside myself rather than outside. Suddenly, there was no more fear, and I let myself fall into that void. I have no recollection of what happened after that....

I was awakened by the chirping of a bird outside the window. I had never heard such a sound before. My eyes were still closed, and I saw the image of a precious diamond.... Yes, if a diamond could make a sound, this is what it would be like. I opened my eyes. The first light of dawn was filtering through the curtains. Without any thought, I felt, I knew, that there is infinitely more to light than we realize. That soft luminosity filtering through the curtains was love itself.... Tears came into my eyes. I got up and walked around the room, and yet I knew that I had never truly seen it before. Everything was fresh and pristine, as if it had just come into existence. I picked up things, a pencil, an empty bottle, marveling at the beauty and aliveness of it all. (Tolle, 1997, pp. 1-2)

These amazing stories show how remarkable the brain's highest experiences can be. Even a fraction of this experience would be significant for anyone. Yet, the point is that anyone *can* experience that level of Awakening, but it helps to be prepared for it. For most of us such a realization is possible only because determined and deliberate practice has prepared us for the experiences that shake up our entrenched ways of being.

The Purposeful Path

Throughout history the small percentage of people who have purposefully tapped into the potential of their higher brain's reality have done so within a religious or spiritual practice. These people would describe the experience in religious or cultural terms because it best explained the nature and cause of their higher reality and the times they lived in. In more recent times, people have found that a secular approach to "mindfulness" has helped them inshift into an Awakening. However, no one belief or faith has any particular advantage in experiencing an inshift and expanded sense of being alive each singular moment.

There are many examples of proactive paths to Awakening that come from spiritual and insight-oriented retreats, places where you are intensely focused on the work of inshifting. The following is an example of what one woman experienced from a disciplined Buddhist practice (from *The Three Pillars of Zen* by Roshi (Zen Master) Philip Kapleau).

> Too stiff and too tired to continue sitting, I slipped quietly from the main hall and returned to the bathhouse for a second bath. Never before had the road been so roadlike, the shops such perfect shops, nor the winter sky so unutterably a starry sky. Joy bubbled up like a fresh spring.
>
> The days and weeks that followed were the most deeply happy and serene of my life. There was no such thing as a 'problem.' Things were either done or not done, but in any case there was neither worry nor consternation. Past relationships to people which once caused me deep disturbance I now saw with perfect understanding. For the first time in my life, I was able to move like the air, in any direction, free at last from the self that had always been such a tormenting bond to me. (Kapleau, 1965, pp. 265-66)

Combining Accidental and Proactive Paths

Which is the best way to Awaken: practice inshifting in difficult times or train every day? Roshi Phillip Kapleau puts it succinctly: "Enlightenment happens by accident. Meditation makes you accident prone."

Awakenings happen naturally when your brain is challenged, but the brain can meet the challenge by radically reorganizing its ways of perceiving and controlling itself. As you practice inshifting and know what each neural inshifting step feels like, you are gradually Awakening. Thus the inevitable life crises that you will face, from death, loss, adolescence, mid-life changes and disabilities, can inshift you even further, jumping you up several rungs on the ladder of psychospiritual development.

How can you best prepare yourself? With a neural-wellness inshifting approach; that is, by learning an approach to inshifting, such as the one offered in this book, and by reorienting the many practices and strategies within six wellness areas—physical, mental, social, cultural, moral and spiritual—to make neural inshifting easier to learn or to happen naturally. With this combined approach, you can enhance the effectiveness of your inshifting and catalyze your chances of Awakening and living a fulfilled and expanded life.

Part 3

Brain Science

The brain is not, like the liver, heart and other internal organs, capable from the moment of birth of all the functions which it ever discharges; for while in common with them, it has certain duties for the exercise of which it is especially intended, its high character in man, as the organ of conscious life, the supreme instrument of his relations with the rest of nature, is developed only by a long and patient training.

— *R. V. Pierce* —

12

The Mind and Brain Problem

You experience everything with your mind,
Your brain has a mind.

You are limited,
Your brain is all but limitless.

You are a slave to habit,
Your brain exists in the moment.

You cope with change.
It flows with change.

You seek happiness and peace,
Your brain exists in joyous peace.

You need security, stability, love, respect and purpose…
It just is.

You take life utterly for granted, and search for meaning,
It experiences being alive right now …
(that is meaning, in itself!).

You seek spiritual Awakening,
While your brain is Awakened.

— Jeff Skolnick —

In medical school and psychiatry residency, students are taught to see how people differ. You learn to categorize diagnoses and treat with the individualized approach or medication that fits the category.

Think about all the different ways people have of being mentally unwell, including depression and anxiety, compulsive eating, addictions to shopping and alcohol, long-term strained relationships with family and friends, the lingering resentment of rough childhoods, and stress about finances. You think: different people, different problems. That's why it took awhile for me to realize that while people and their problems are different, there is a common theme to their suffering (even for people with obvious psychiatric brain illnesses like biological depression).

The problem, as I have said, lies in the configuration of our brains. We are fooled and controlled by the lower aspects of our brain. These lower areas process the senses and what they trigger, our body states and drives, our mind activity like thoughts, mental image and emotions, and our physical movements. The lower brain areas can function as a collective fairly autonomously. There are kinds of seizures, for instance, that occur while people are awake that cause them to speak, move, experience "forced thinking," panic or desire, all automatically. From reflex driving to being stuck in a one dimensional life role, your lower brain can do pretty much everything it takes for someone to go through life. Not well, but well enough to survive.

These functions of the lower brain can readily dominate the higher aspects of our brain—higher awareness and intentional self-direction. When, in early adulthood, our higher brain areas develop the full capacity for neural inshifting, we need to learn how to intentionally inshift to continue developing to the fullest experience of life of which we are capable.

Your mind is the prevalent aspect of your lower brain that you experience as "you." The mind is software for the brain's hardware. It helps the brain think, imagine, judge, interpret and process emotionally. This is obviously crucial to survival, and so the mind is extremely powerful. It easily overrides instincts and intuition. It helps your brain believe in things, make decisions, project itself as an "I" into the world to solve problems and plan into the future. Your mind gives the brain an identity that provides unity to your experience, connecting past to future. In fact, the mind can serve as a lens through which all of your experiences are screened and oriented.

Sensory triggers are also very powerful in their own right. A sudden loud noise can scare you and influence your mood. Pain can make you irritable and rash and ruin your quality of life. Certain colors can be overstimulating or influence your mood and decisions. Hunger, sex drives, fatigue and other body drives likewise can exert control over your thoughts, feelings and actions, without your conscious control.

Because the lower brain is so powerful it can easily dominate the brain's highest functions, determining what we are aware of, what we choose and how we act. As you might imagine, this inevitably creates real problems.

The first problem is that lower brain reality is not the highest reality there is. It is the experience of reality organized in ways that can be described in words, colored by body drives and triggered by sense triggers. To the extent that the lower brain takes over, you can live in a reality that is self-delusional or even psychotic. Most people have experienced how their minds can jump to false conclusions, putting them in a drama that they later realize was overblown or completely unreal. A lower brain reality is certainly not one of your conscious choosing.

Besides the fact that it is not the highest reality there is, another problem with lower brain dominance is that the lower brain is easily programmable. Your sensory triggers, body drives and mind can be *easily* programmed by other people, early childhood, life events, even familiarity and repetition. That can make you vulnerable to the influences of people who don't have your best interests at heart, and it makes you as authentic as a puppet on a string, stuck in patterns and less effective in negotiating life.

The lower brain is prone to experience everything in categories, such as "good," "bad," "pleasurable," "painful," "beautiful," "about me," "useful to me," and "irrelevant," so that you miss much of what is sublime, interesting, fascinating, and even exquisite and amazing about the world in-between those categories. That can make life feel dull, boring, empty and ultimately meaningless.

As we've said, your lower brain's dominance keeps you at a lower level of psychospiritual development. In fact, the vast majority of humans alive now or who have ever lived are largely controlled by their lower brain instead of in control of it, a fact most people don't know or do not completely understand. As a result, we develop unhealthy traits, get trapped into compulsive behaviors and become fixed in narrow ways of being in the world, inflexible and self-absorbed.

Lower brain dominance leads to fear, anger, anxiety, anguish, depression and stress—in short, it makes us suffer. When we become aware enough to see our mind and its attachments, we are liberated from stress and suffering. We can come to a higher, wondrous insight and a healthier place inside.

In actuality, your senses, body states, mind and programmed actions (SBMA) are not really separate, as we've said; they can function as a collective, although it's unruly and often the collective is internally fragmented and at odds within itself. Specifically, your mind can control your body drives, making you sleepy, hungry or sexually aroused just by thinking or imagining. Think of hypnosis causing you to sleep. Remember the Rorschach inkblot test? A neutral inkblot can look like food and make you hungry. (It's more likely to look like food if you're already hungry. It works both ways.)

Senses, mind, body states and actions can and do all trigger each other, compelling you to act and experience without your conscious awareness.

As we'll explore in much more depth in the next chapter,

your higher brain consists of the ability to know you are aware of anything, to realize you exist right now, and then deliberately plan, choose and act based on that level of awareness. Higher awareness and self-direction, that's really who or what you are deep inside.

Of course, we've known for ages that senses, body states, mind and automatic actions can override conscious reason and behavior, and that this control is the cause of stress and suffering. Philosophers, psychologists, healers and religious traditions have reported this higher-lower brain dynamic for centuries. They used philosophical concepts like "man's higher nature," Western religious notions of moral strength and sin, psychological theories like conditioned responses and motivation, and even Eastern spiritual ideas of mindfulness. Not too often are the everyday struggles of people described from the perspective of their brains—of the competition between the lower and higher areas that we'll explore here in Part 3.

Can this dominance be permanently changed? Nothing is permanent, of course, but you'll see how inshifting can lead to a semi-permanent re-balancing of higher and lower brain areas, and to an Awakening. However, before you embark on your journey inward, learning about the brain and the model of how the higher and lower brain areas interact may make it easier for you to learn how to inshift.

13

An Amazing Organ

We have in us the power to transcend the bounds of
our narrow individuality, and to find ourselves in that
which seems to lie beyond us.

— John Caird —

It is unmatched in its ability to think,
to communicate, and to reason. Most striking of all,
it has a unique awareness of its identity and of its place
in space and time. Welcome to the human brain,
the cathedral of complexity.

— Peter Coveney and Roger Highfield —

Floating in your head, right now, you have unquestionably the most complex structure in the universe: your brain. This small three or so pound fatty gelatinous tissue is so phenomenally complex that, right now, it can see and is reading and comprehending the strange ink patterns that make these words. But it is not just reading individual words, it is understanding the meaning of groups of words put together, comprehending the sentences in moving images, hearing its own internal reading voice, anticipating what is coming next in the sentence, and so on.

Your brain also creates art, understands what to an ape would be unimaginably difficult concepts, and invents new solutions to complex problems. It can then register it all in awareness, cognizant to varying degrees of what is happening at any given moment.

That's miraculous, isn't it? But as incredible as that is, a computer can be programmed to process, analyze, create and even register experiences and simulate features of awareness. Besides, many lower animals are aware on some level of what is happening. This is regular awareness—that you can remember what you experienced, and that it registered in your memory, like a witness testifying in court.

Yet there's something else your human brain does that is even more astonishing than its exquisite creativity, profound intelligence and awareness! It's a function usually invisible and forsaken, lingering in the background of your daily experience, one you probably didn't fully realize you had: your brain can reflect on its own awareness! I call this reflective awareness. Two aspects of reflective awareness are that your brain can know *what* it is knowing, and that it can know *that* it is knowing; or, another way of putting the latter is that it can know it is alive in any particular moment.

To know *what* you are aware of means to be purposefully aware of something in particular. For example, think about the chair you're sitting on. Feel it beneath you. You know you're sitting on it. And if I asked you about it in half an hour, you would know you were sitting on it—you could recall that knowing. The awareness of the chair registers somewhere in your brain, so it can be called into your active attention at any time or remembered later. That's regular awareness. Yet you probably weren't that aware of the chair until I just asked you. Now that I am calling your attention to it, you are *aware of being aware* of the chair. That's one aspect of reflective awareness—an active knowing that you are aware of something in particular.

Your brain can also know that it knows, without any specific thing to focus on. That's a higher degree of reflective awareness: awareness of having any awareness. It means the brain is actually focusing its attention inwards, so that it knows that it is conscious. Regardless of what you are experiencing, knowing that you know means being aware of the fact that there is awareness happening. This is roughly the same thing as saying your brain can know it's alive in this very moment! Reflective awareness is what neural inshifting develops.

Think about that for a moment. As I mentioned in Part 1, this is a biological organ, built of organic chemicals, the same ones your liver or heart tissue is made from. Yet, it can be aware, it can be aware of being aware and it can know it exists. It's amazing to just imagine that degree of complexity, let alone to experience it firsthand. That's potentially life-altering. It's the core experience of Awakening.

Again, there are degrees of knowing—the highest degree, reflective consciousness, comes from those higher brain areas that are underused by the vast majority of people. You may ordinarily go through the day aware of many things, but really fully cognizant of very little. Our reflective awareness is not developed, and so when it is used, it is so taken for granted it is practically invisible. Yet, if you were to develop those higher brain areas and really pay attention to the process of being alive, you would realize more in each moment on a very deep level what it means that you are alive, that you made it into existence! That's the meaning and ecstasy of an Awakening.

Just to be clear, reflective awareness is sometimes called self-awareness, which is confusing, because reflective awareness has nothing to do with being aware of a personalized, subjective identity or a "self." Reflective awareness simply means being aware of the process; it is an impersonal process that experiences existing. To be reflectively aware, one way or another, you have to inshift. It's one of the fundamental aspects of neural inshifting: to be able to step "back" from or "outside" of regular awareness to know the process of being aware.

The capacity of your brain for reflective awareness results from the evolutionary arrival of some of its newest parts, which reside in the outer layers of the upper brain called the neocortex (or new cortex). These highest areas of the brain are the most recently evolved. They likely distinguish the human brain from the brains of its closest primate relatives. The neocortex has areas that are responsible for reflective awareness as well as conscious choice and control. The cortex is an outer layer that surrounds and can direct the inner parts of your brain—the ones responsible for primitive and built-in functions like instincts for self-protection and aggression or regulation of bodily functions.

Knowing "knowing" is an extra step of awareness. It requires milliseconds more processing time. Yet, if that ability is used more often and developed it can ground you firmly in the moment. It gives you the reference point from which to have context of this particular time in your life. It leads you to greater wisdom, emotional maturity, empathy, and so on. And, because reflective awareness must be purposeful or deliberate to function, it has a twin: volition, intention, or, more commonly, will.

Intention is the capacity to consciously choose what to do or how to think, feel, react, plan or deliberately guide yourself through an action or series of actions of mind and body. The more conscious your choice and actions, the more reflective awareness is being used. The twin functions of reflective awareness and intention arise from each other. They require each other to function and to be developed. Both arise from your higher brain. Both are the essential elements of neural inshifting.

What is reflective awareness used for—besides Awakening to sublime, taken-for-granted realities? Reflective awareness tells you, first and foremost, that you are awake and not dreaming. That's pretty basic. It also gives you many other abilities, such as the ability to know when you are "not acting like yourself," or in an unusual mood when you are, say, affected by hormonal changes or intoxication. It helps you pull your mind out of a scary movie, as well as giving you the greatest sense of meaning and purpose and a profound feeling of inner peace and joy.

Depending on how much reflective awareness and volition are in play (as a result of your natural or learned ability to inshift) you will move up and down the range of levels of reality. (You learned about that in Part 2.) Reflective awareness, because it allows you to be objective towards your mind and the other aspects of your lower brain, creates the experience of there being more than one "you." The lower or ordinary "you" is mainly just aware. The higher, inshifted "you" is reflectively aware. The difference is this extra step of awareness that you get when you inshift.

A higher degree of reflective awareness can pop up in flashes during exceptional life moments when you might stop and think, "Wow, this is really me. I'm here, really doing this." For instance, the first time you drive alone, or when it dawns on you that you are actually a parent, or when you know you are going to die, these are times when you step back and know that you are experiencing.

Reflective awareness is experienced from deeper inside you. That may be a subtle thing to notice, but inshifting will make that more obvious. If reflective awareness were fully developed you would be a step removed from the things in your awareness, aware, as we said, more of the process itself. That ability to, in a way, "step back" from your senses, body states and mind lets you realize their illusory nature. That's because *nothing* can be more real than the process of being aware! It is the one and only thing that you can hang on to, no matter what is happening in your mind or your body. Whether you are in a virtual reality machine, having hallucinations or half asleep, to borrow from René Descartes (who said, "I think, therefore I am"): "I reflect on my awareness, therefore I am."

As you will see in the neural inshifting steps, instead of experiencing senses, body, mind and actions as the be-all and end-all of objective reality, they appear more simulated by your brain. A highly inshifted, Awakened perception is of a "brain reality" or neural reality. Within that virtual, neural reality your reflective awareness puts you squarely in an eternally present now. Your brain grasps the profound fact of its existence. Everything is experienced relative to that presence. That process of knowing, which is the higher "you," possesses insight into events, maturity and appreciation and has you behave with more complete authenticity. Only neural inshifting, which makes the fullest use of your higher brain, can take you from who you think you are to the amazing reality of what you really are.

To more fully understand the science of neural inshifting let's delve now into the neurophysiology of the brain and find the neuronal cells that create awareness and volition.

14

The Seeds of Your Higher Brain: A Hypothesis

An introcosm that is more myself than anything I can find in a mirror. This consciousness that is myself of selves, that is everything, yet nothing at all—what is it? And where did it come from? And why?

— Julian Jaynes —

As we begin the 21st century, the Hubble space telescope is providing us with information about as yet uncharted regions of the universe and the promise that we may learn something about the origin of the cosmos. This same spirit of adventure is also being directed to the most complex structure that exists in the universe—the human brain.

— Floyd E. Bloom —

The theory that led to my models of neural inshifting began with my study of the brain during my graduate neuropsychology program. Somewhere deep within the microscopic cells or neurons of the brain lays the very genesis of awareness and reflective awareness. There are many theories of how consciousness arose and where it is seated. Here is mine. For some readers, it may shed more light on the practice of neural inshifting and make it that much more understandable. For others, this much information may be a distraction. If that is you, I suggest you skip over this chapter and possibly even the next.

There are two sides to the human brain. Viewed from the top (see Figure 3) each side is really a separate brain, each capable of its own awareness, each with its own way of viewing reality, its own language. Each side of the brain is arranged so that the motor cortex (that initiates action) is in front and the sensory areas (that receive stimulation from the senses) are in the rear part of the brain.

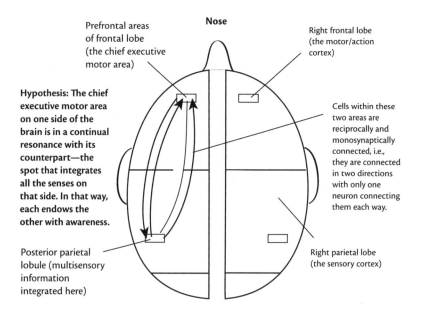

Prefrontal areas of frontal lobe (the chief executive motor area)

Nose

Right frontal lobe (the motor/action cortex)

Hypothesis: The chief executive motor area on one side of the brain is in a continual resonance with its counterpart—the spot that integrates all the senses on that side. In that way, each endows the other with awareness.

Cells within these two areas are reciprocally and monosynaptically connected, i.e., they are connected in two directions with only one neuron connecting them each way.

Posterior parietal lobule (multisensory information integrated here)

Right parietal lobe (the sensory cortex)

Figure 3. Brain cells (neurons) combine to create awareness on each side of the brain

The central control area of the motor cortex is the prefrontal area. Those cells are the chief action area, planning actions into the future, choosing or inhibiting action. They deal not just with specific actions, but responses of all kinds, thinking as well as moving.

The cells responsible for sensory integration from all the senses are areas further towards the back of the brain, in areas on each side called the posterior parietal lobules. They don't specialize, but receive all sensory information so they can integrate them, putting them together as a whole.

Brain cells in both these cortical areas—the prefrontal lobe and posterior parietal lobules on each side of your brain—are linked in a unique way for the brain: they are reciprocally and monosynaptically connected (which means one grouping of nerve cells connect these areas extending each way from the back to the front)! That's a long way for a single nerve cell to stretch. A synapse is the space where one nerve cell links to another. This means that motor nerve cells from the prefrontal area reach all the way to the posterior parietal lobule, and vice versa.

My hypothesis is that there is a resonance between certain prefrontal cells and the posterior lobule cells. That is, there are extremely rapid back-and-forth, round-robin nerve firings that make these areas meld into one unit, like watching a fan whirl around looking like a single disc. The result is that each area endows the other with both consciousness and intention. Each area contributes an action and sensory piece that helps the other come "alive" with awareness and be able to deliberately act.

Yet, these aren't the only two players in this scheme. These four areas (two on each side) are coordinated by the thalamus, a collection of cells in the middle part of the brain whose job is to coordinate activity between different areas of the brain. I propose that it sets the balance between these two areas. (See Figure 4.) If the resonance leans more towards the motor or prefrontal side, then awareness is based more in doing something, like scanning or interpreting the environment. If the balance is set towards the sensory or posterior parietal areas, then awareness is more of a passive sensory experience. And, if the left and right sides of these pairs are not set in the same way, then the two halves of the brain will be discordant and function more separately.

Here's another factor in this dynamic within and between the cerebral hemispheres (sides of the brain). The thalamus also relays energy to these areas so they can function by receiving stimulation from the reticular activating system (RAS). The RAS is a tangle of nerve cells that surround the brain stem. The brain stem gets incoming nerve fibers from the spinal cord. The main function of the central neurons of the brain stem is to relay information about pain, temperature, touch, sound and eyesight to the sensory areas of the cortex. The RAS, however, gets collateral branches off of this central brain stem purely for stimulation or arousal purposes. It provides the energy, like a battery turning on a flashlight.

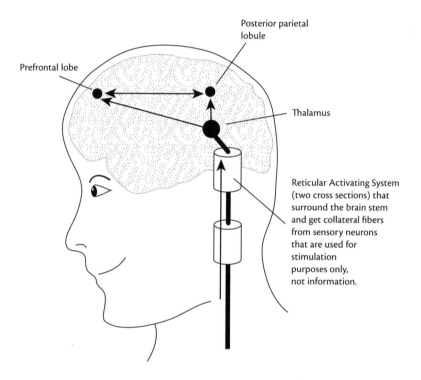

Figure 4. Hypothesized structures in the brain that create awareness

According to Julian Jaynes in *The Origin of Consciousness in the Breakdown of the Bicameral Mind*, the function of the Reticular Activating System "is to sensitize or 'awaken' selected nervous circuits and desensitize others.... It is the place where general anesthesia produces its effect by deactivating its neurons. Cutting it produces permanent sleep and coma. Stimulating it through an implanted electrode in most of its regions wakes up a sleeping animal." (Jaynes, 1976)

Therefore, my hypothesis is that these six main elements—two prefrontal and two posterior parietal lobules, the central thalamus and RAS—together create regular awareness.

What does this have to do with neural inshifting? First, neural inshifting is involved in resetting the balance point between the prefrontal and posterior parietal cells; the motor and sensory areas that I hypothesized endow each other with awareness. Neural inshifting resets an imbalance that favors the motor side of the equation (this happens more on the left or dominant hemisphere). I'll explain.

Earlier in human evolution, before we developed higher awareness to the extent that it is today, we spent more time sensing the environment and were better aware of our surroundings. We sensed the air pressure and humidity, wind, temperature, sounds, sights, inner instincts and emotions at the same time. With the development of reflective awareness along with the increasing demands of civilization, we have relied increasingly on the motor cortex to categorize things with language, make more and more decisions and constantly act, act, act. As a result, we rely on the motor aspect of awareness, changing the balance in awareness on each side of the brain. Our need to scan the environment for specific things that signal reward or consequence (such as billboards, road conditions while driving, TV and multitasking) has limited our awareness so that we have difficulty just sensing, just being.

The sensory-motor imbalance on both sides of our brain that has been created by an increasingly hyperactive civilization has also affected which side of the brain we use as well. Because, in most people, the left half of the brain is dominated by spoken language (a motor-dominated function) we have come to rely on language to be aware of things. The right side of the brain is dominated by emotional comprehension and expression and includes the enhanced ability to sense things in their entirety, as a whole. We don't access that ability as much because we are so focused on details and specific tasks. As a result, most people use their left hemispheres for explicit motor-dominated awareness. That's another kind of imbalance that makes awareness an action more than a sensory experience. Our awareness has become co-opted by language and a linear way of perceiving things. We increasingly use the left hemisphere for its awareness.

Any self-regulation practice for the brain needs to help set a new balance between its sensory and motor aspects. Changing that balance will affect both the front-back balance as well as the left-right balance. That is why the neural inshifting steps involve experiencing your senses, body states, mind activity and actions as pure energy without interpretation. That helps to reset that balance. Resetting that balance changes many facets of our experience and behavior.

This rebalancing entails learning to regulate the switching point that the thalamus controls. That's done, in part, by learning to regulate arousal (stimulation). Waking yourself up from the inside and experiencing energy (they actually go hand-in-hand) are skills that happen below the level of language. They are experienced, much like balancing on one foot, without the direction of spoken language. You can talk to yourself and coach yourself on how to balance on one foot, but really, to easily find and stay balanced, you need to stop talking and just feel the balance inside. It's some internal ability that defies language, that you find deeper within, which is part of what it means to practice neural inshifting. It entails letting go of the total motor dominance that we are used to and being in a greater receptive mode, aware of the entirety of any given moment. That is a central trick to neural inshifting: to be able to let go of your heavy reliance on your motor system to experience life and learn to experience the energy of your sensory system, which cannot be categorized or defined in language.

So far, we've spoken about the regulation of regular awareness on each side of the brain (and how resetting the sensory-motor balance on each side can help each side coordinate better with the other). My hypothesis continues on from there. Remember, my supposition is that regular awareness—awareness of what is going on without any extra reflective knowing—is what you get on each side. How then, you might ask, do you get reflective awareness (knowing that you know)?

Reflective awareness is like having stereoscopic vision instead of monocular vision. Let's consider the communication between the hemispheres. The corpus callosum is a bundle of fibers connecting each hemisphere which are sometimes surgically severed as a treatment to prevent intractable seizures from spreading. Evidence from people who had their corpus callosum cut shows that each hemisphere has its own awareness, its own way of expressing itself. Each hemisphere can be ignorant of the other. I believe that it takes both hemispheres of the brain working in concert with each other, aware of each other, to have reflective awareness.

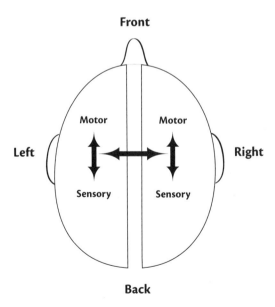

Figure 5. Coordination of cerebral hemispheres for reflective awareness

How do you coordinate the awarenesses on each side of your brain? Two ways. First, as we'll explore in the neural inshifting steps in Part 4, the act of rebalancing the sensory-motor scales on each side of the brain (raising the sensory side by taking in the energy of the SBMA and lowering the motor side by letting go) also acts to coordinate the two hemispheres. Second, the last neural inshifting step explicitly shows how to pay attention to an inner location and the experience of being alive in the now. That directly uses both of your cerebral hemispheres to find reflective awareness. (See Figure 5.)

You will see aspects of this hypothesis in every neural inshifting step. You'll see it by allowing your awareness to be stimulated by input instead of predominantly informed by it. You'll see it in the skill of releasing language-dominated control for an inner sensory-mediated higher control. You'll see it in the open clarity that houses reflective awareness, because it is beyond information.

15

The Neurosoteriology Model

*It is essential to understand our brains in some detail
if we are to assess correctly our place in this vast and
complicated universe we see all around us.*

— *Francis Crick* —

Earlier in my career I developed a broader model of how the
brain works that I called the neurosoteriology model. "Neuro" stands for the nervous system or the brain. "Soteriology" has
been used to describe the study of religious states as salvation,
enlightenment or Awakening. Neurosoteriology, in this sense, is
the study of the brain as it undergoes an Awakening.

When I first developed this model it described what I thought
happened to the brain during meditation as it advanced towards
spiritual states. The model is now much broader and includes
the whole range of human states of experience and functioning,
from primitive, dysfunctional states to the highest levels of maturity (states that are only supranormal because they aren't yet the
norm), experience and behavior, i.e. the so-called spiritual levels.

Once I could describe what happens in the brain the next
task was to use that model to explain what happens on a subjective or inside-out personal level. I then created the idea of neural
inshifting, based on the same principles of meditation that I had
learned before. Except that neural inshifting is clearer, brain-
based and *portable*! It does not require the special circumstances
of sitting in formal meditation. Neural inshifting is a skill that
is described by the neurosoteriology model as central to healing and higher development. The neurosoteriology model shows

how inshifting enhances an ordinary day or helps people cope with normal life challenges. It also shows how it can be used to help people better manage their moods, reactions to stress and unhealthy beliefs (even hallucinations and delusions). And, while bettering your daily life and helping you to heal, the model shows how the skill of neural inshifting can take you to advanced states of being and experiencing.

To understand the background and underlying brain mechanisms of neural inshifting is to understand neurosoteriology. The neurosoteriology model starts by describing how the brain can be divided into lower and higher areas. We spoke about the neurophysiological details of what makes up the higher brain areas in the last chapter. Here, we speak about the higher vs. lower brain areas in a more general sense.

The Higher Brain Areas

Recall that the higher areas of your brain are those executive areas that give you the twin abilities of reflective awareness (remember, knowing that you are aware of something and knowing that you are aware of anything or knowing you are alive each moment) and volition (conscious intention and choice, spontaneous action and intuitive reasoning). These are the ingredients of the deeper experiences of being "you." More than your quirky personality or even what you think and do, your higher brain gives you the most fundamental information possible: the sense of being an alive being that can self-direct the myriad parts of its mind and body.

Like a high watt light bulb, your higher brain needs more amps of stimulation coursing through it to function to its fullest. The more energy that makes it to your higher brain, the better it works. When it is working to its fullest, it becomes reflectively aware of its own functioning. The flow of sensory, body and mind triggers is more apt to be experienced as they enter awareness, and as they trigger a sensory, body state, mind or action response. With this level of awareness, though, you are in more control (self-direction or macromanagerial control) rather than lower or micromanagerial control. As you are more reflectively aware, you can more easily direct what response will be triggered or whether a brand-new response is needed.

Reflective awareness causes your higher brain to use *inclusive attention* to sense its SBMA, as opposed to the *exclusive attention* your lower brain uses. Your higher brain is more inclusive of what it is aware of in each moment, which includes the process of being aware.

Experiencing sensory, body and mind triggers as energy allows your higher brain to avoid focusing exclusively on the information value of these triggers so that they don't automatically trigger a preset response. Volition (will or intention) is then better able to manage and direct the body, mind and action response.

In essence, using inclusive attention that leads to reflective awareness, your higher brain helps you Awaken to the miracle of your existence. That is the key to the health, happiness and wondrous insights of Awakening. Your higher brain gives you the control to manage the triggering of responses by stimuli so that you can be more successful in life, with intention, spontaneity and intuitiveness.

The Lower Brain Areas

Drive a car on the freeway while you're daydreaming, imbibe enough alcohol to act like you would never normally act, find yourself jumping to conclusions based on scant evidence, be controlled by a hypnotic suggestion—experience all these and you'll understand what it means, first hand, to not be in full conscious control and to function with little or low awareness.

The lower areas of your brain, acting together, can manage all the basic things that you need to do to get through life. It's like the brain of a sophisticated robot that is controlled by the built-in programs and the algorithmic sequences (if this, then this) of artificial intelligence. Philosopher George Gurjieff called it "the machine."

Most everyone knows that the lower brain controls body functions, but studies show that basic thinking, analyzing, imagining; how you react to people, events and things around you; and your emotions can all occur with little or no awareness. Even with a bit more awareness that is functioning and registers events, but is passive, your lower brain can still largely control your personality, beliefs and attitudes, the experience of an identity and the way you interpret your senses. When you sing or dance, read or write, do simple calculations, solve problems or create art, whatever you can do and be, regardless of how much awareness there is, your lower brain is the workhorse. The question is whether it controls itself or whether you, your higher brain, controls it.

The Interplay Between Lower and Higher Brain Areas

Of course, we're never just fully our higher or lower brain. (See Figure 6.) They combine in different degrees, giving rise to different "you's" depending on how much of each brain area is in control.

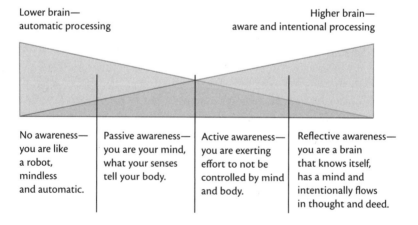

Figure 6. Levels of experience and behavior based on higher and lower brain involvement

With the lower brain areas in much greater control, you are a robot. Like an animal that reacts in blind fear or a machine that is programmed to accomplish tasks, "you" are not fully home, so to speak. That's you with no or very low awareness. With awareness that is simple or passive "you" are the lens of your mind. What you believe, who you are, how you react, how and what you experience feels real, as if you are the boss. Except that competing thoughts and feelings determine who you are. Information that signals pain and pleasure, and your body and mind's motivation to avoid pain and to have pleasure (also information), rule who you are. That's what the lower brain area does. It creates an "information"-based reality.

I'm not saying that your lower brain should never be in control. In a dire emergency, your lower brain ought to get most of the arousal energy, so that you will whip your hand off of a hot stove before you even know it. On the other hand, the buzz of a fly will grab your attention more than the details of an important lecture, when your higher brain is not functioning enough. You'll glance at an attractive body in a bathing suit, not the road. And ultimately your life will have passed you by with little more than a surface experience of being alive without the full functioning of your higher brain.

For the most part, though, your higher brain needs to be in control, if for no other reason than it is more adaptive. It's the part that resists the impulse to smack someone who makes you angry. It's also the center of your happiness and fulfillment in life and of your mental and physical health.

In essence, this interplay between higher and lower brain areas is what 19th-century Nobel prize-winning neurophysiologist Sir Charles Sherrington called a "reciprocity" (a see-sawing). Calling the executive function of reflective awareness and intention "mind" (a paradoxical term in this book) and automatic behavior simply "reflex," he said: "Between reflex and mind there is a reciprocity. The more reflex the reflex, the less does mind accompany it." (See Figure 7.)

As seen in Figure 7, you can imagine the lower and higher brains as balanced on a see-saw, with the lower brain capable of only basic experience and behaviors while the higher brain is more intelligent, capable of more subtle perceptions and highly nuanced behaviors. Learning to inshift is learning to keep your lower brain from grabbing hold of your attention (which it does 99% of the time) so that you don't react without full awareness and conscious intent. It is to inhibit reflexes or direct them into spontaneous action.

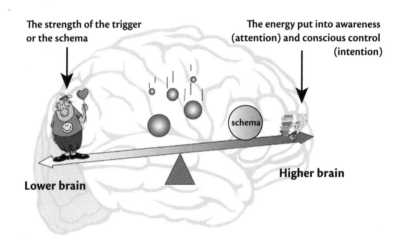

Figure 7. The see-saw balance between the lower brain and higher brain

The Ball on the See-Saw: The Schema Connection Between Stimulus and Response

Your brain is made of trillions of nerve cells and can store an astronomical amount of information. Information may be a bit different than what you think. I define it as connections. Connections are learned data stored in your brain as units of memories, behaviors, attitudes and other psychological reactions. Or, information is the connection between the sensory, body and mind stimuli that directly triggers the hardwired nerve cells that lead to reflexes and instincts. From the simplest reflex to the most nuanced and complex idea there are many levels and kinds of connections between a stimulus and a response. The smallest unit of a stored connection is called a schema, or its plural, schemata (see how the see-saw in Figure 7 processes schemata differently depending on which part it is on). Your higher and lower brain regulation systems vie for control of schemata. They vie for control of the connections processed within and between your SBMA. (Your higher brain can also "just experience" without any schemata, but that is an exceptional state of inshifting that is part of Awakening, not the rule.)

Schemata link stimuli with one response, although one particular stimulus can trigger multiple schema responses. You can learn to connect a ringing sound to an image of a bell, gong or telephone, to the word "bell," to excitement if you were expecting a telephone call, or to a plain startled jump with an unexpected loud ring. Every moment, thousands of stimuli act as information of sorts, triggering tens of thousands of schemata in your brain. Again, this processing between a stimulus and a response happens either with the software of learned memories or by the hardware of instincts and reflexes. Whether you blink, think or wink is determined by which stimulus is linked to which behavior and by how much your awareness and intent can intervene!

Of course, we are not earthworms that have simple repertoires of behavior. A million bits of stimuli come into your brain each moment, many triggering some form of schema. Each one schema is then linked to other schemata in cascading chains of information and instructions that make up your behavior and experience. You ride a bicycle based on the grouping of learned schemata and by how much attention you are paying to what you are doing. Chains and clusters of schemata being triggered in different circumstances can create new schemata (learning). That's how artificial intelligence can evolve and learn without awareness. Your lower brain is intelligent enough to learn. It is these cascading chains and clusters of schemata that create different aspects of your personality with their own memories and beliefs, for example, the "fun free-spirited you" and the "serious no-nonsense you."

The information value of what you experience comes from the schemata in your brain being either triggered or created and changed every moment. That is the projector and film that creates your lower brain reality. As neural inshifting accesses more of your higher brain functions it can change your reality as you increasingly distance yourself from the information value of stimuli and experience both triggers and responses as energy (before they trigger off more schemata).

The two factors affecting schemata are shown in Figure 7. They are the strength of the trigger, or schema, and the energy put into awareness (attention) and conscious control (intention). The see-saw between the lower brain and higher brain tilts according to which schema gets to be expressed and how it is expressed (automatically, through the lower brain, or creatively, with the higher brain's direction).

Whether what you had for dinner last night pops into your head, a friendly discussion turns into an angry argument, or you get up and walk out right now from wherever you are, in fact, your entire attitude and outlook depend on the forces of the automatic processes of your lower brain and the executive functioning of your higher brain. These two forces determine "who" you are, whether and which schema or groupings of schemata get to rise up from your brain and become "Tom" or "Sue." Whether a schema is processed automatically or with executive functions depends not just on how aware you are, but also on the strength of what triggers the schema (a loud noise or graphic photograph), combined with the power loaded into the schema itself (such as the sight of your mother-in-law who has been very critical of you). In the face of a powerful stimulus and powerful associations, not many people can choose to avoid flinching, for instance, when someone else's hand is quickly moved towards their face.

You can, of course, choose to remember, feel or do what you want when you pay attention and make a conscious choice. You can choose not to flinch. You can also choose what to think. Yet there are degrees to which you can be aware and choose. That's a major point in neural inshifting, because most people are not nearly as conscious as they think they are, particularly when it comes to thinking, feeling and believing. This is the interplay that you must come to terms with as you inshift, the gray area common to most peoples' lives, where your awareness is active but subordinate to your mind. Who you *think* you are is a collection of triggered schemata, but what you *really* are is the process—the awareness and the intention—that experiences "aliveness now" and that directs responding. The trick: live in a world that requires you to have an identity and negotiate its rules while keeping the higher perspective that isn't fooled into believing that is reality.

Again, high awareness and intention require energy to course through your higher brain. To bring energy soaring through your higher brain, stretch your attention so that it attends to what is happening outwardly while it is also turned inward. That's a significant part of neural inshifting: redirecting attention so energy flows with it, and redirecting energy so attention goes with it.

Here are some examples of how you can bring the energy of arousal into your higher brain. Think about putting your hand in hot water, coming out of a dark room into bright sunlight or standing close to the speakers at a rock concert—no matter how subtle, your senses arouse you. To get that arousal to your higher brain, experience your senses as energy rather than information. Relax a bit and let all your senses in, let them stimulate you and fill your head with pleasant energy.

Arousal also comes from within your body, such as your nervous and gland systems. Your adrenal glands pump out adrenaline when you're frightened. Your thyroid tells all your cells to burn off more energy for your use. The sympathetic side of your nervous system revs you up to "fight or flight." It can be artificially revved up with a cup of coffee or a diet pill. You can feel those sources of energy in a way that lets them stimulate you to alertness.

Arousal energy also comes from your mind. Whether thinking about someone you love but haven't seen for awhile, looking at an image of war and feeling horrified, or seeing the flag and feeling pride, these are ways your emotions and thoughts can arouse you. Without judging them as good or bad, you can let them fill your head with stimulation. The act of paying attention to these activities of your mind as sources of energy and then drawing them in is how you bring energy into your higher brain.

In fact all these sources of arousal can be shunted up to your higher brain, so that they stimulate it as much as if not more than lower brain SBMA activity.

Beware, the power of the trigger itself and the power embedded in the schema connection are important to understand and come to terms with. Whether a bright light triggers a wince, you remember something that reminds you of some humiliation you experienced, or your kids "push your buttons," the *strength of the schema connection* can determine whether you are in control or controlled … unless it's directed along using detached awareness! Whether you are centered and objective in an argument with someone you don't like, or you're replacing an old habit for a new repertoire, you must be reflectively aware of (objectively aware of) the force of that schema connection.

Perhaps the most powerful and difficult chain of schemata to Awaken from is the "I" expressed by your internal voice—that constant stream of narration so ingrained in your "lower you" experience of life that it colors, influences and controls everything you see and do.

Because the lower areas of your brain, which are made up of

schemata, don't need your awareness or conscious direction to function they have a major advantage in controlling you. Habits are hard to unlearn for that reason. Ingrained personality traits, such as pessimism, are hard to change. Neural inshifting is the path to Awaken from the controlling illusions of your lower brain to a life of objective maturity and present wonderment.

Having the see-saw begin to lean predominantly to the right (in Figure 7, toward the higher brain) requires that you become adept at neural inshifting. However you accomplish this and whatever you call it (as there are many ways to mature and Awaken), the underlying mechanism always involves neural inshifting. Whether you learn it directly or indirectly, or call it something else. And it is always a work in progress. Circumstances and your lower brain continually present new challenges to your inshifting. So the see-saw will always go back and forth. It's never, ever stationary. Schemata, such as points of view, habits and memories, are always created and provide a never-ending and fascinating challenge to manage. Neural inshifting entails not only moving the see-saw to tilt to the higher brain in each moment, but recognizing that over time there is a see-sawing and resonance that happens in patterns.

A daily practice of neural inshifting prepares you for the inevitable crises of life. With time, neural inshifting will become the vehicle that Awakens you to a higher, healthier and more fulfilling reality.

Now let's learn how to inshift.

Part 4

The Skill of Neural Inshifting

However, when we shift our awareness or "frequency"
from self-consciousness—where fear, impossibility or
feelings of separation reside—to cosmic consciousness,
which is in total harmony with the universe and where
none of those feelings exist, then anything is possible.

— Rhonda Byrne —

16

Inshifting Scenarios

*You can become blind by seeing each day as a
similar one. Each day is a different one, each day
brings a miracle of its own. It's just a matter
of paying attention to this miracle.*

— *Paul Coelho* —

*Y*ou're walking home when the weather turns cold and rainy, and
after a half hour, drenched, tired and cold, you finally get home.
Shivering, you start a hot bath and get out of your wet clothes.

The moment your foot enters the bathwater, twinges of exhilaration and relaxation flow through your body. As you immerse yourself,
the blanket of heat envelops your body. You think to yourself how
incredibly good this feels.

Lying there in the bath, it occurs to you, "I should take a bath
every day." And then to more fully benefit from this special moment,
you decide to try to relax even more into it, thinking, "I should turn
on some relaxing music to really enjoy this." You just sit back and
your mind starts going over the day, picturing the miserable half hour
you spent trying to get home and how great the bath is. You don't ever
want to leave. As your mind keeps running through the day's events,
you start getting sleepy...

Then a neural inshift happens.

You cause the warm water to wake you up rather than lull you
into drowsiness and fantasy. With your attention detached from any
one thing, you can better feel the hot water massaging your skin, the
dim light in the bathroom, the vision of yourself in the water, the
tinkling sound of the water being moved about, the inner exhilara-

tion. One unified experience, you are now also bathing in a field of energy. That feels good beyond the warmth of the bath. This is a new kind of pleasure—a crisp aliveness in your head and a rushing release of energy. You realize this moment is complete. The next moment will extend from this one.

You are a high school basketball player. It's the final game of the year. The score is tied, with only seconds to go.

Suddenly you get knocked down, a shrill whistle pierces the air, and the ref assigns a penalty shot to you. It could determine the outcome of the game and the series.

Up for the penalty shot, you're standing there looking at the hoop, both teams lined up watching you, the crowds whooping and screaming. You're nervous. Your heart is racing. You fear embarrassment. Holding the ball above your head ... you realize you have a choice: let the insecurity bring you down, control how you shoot the ball, or let the energy of the crowd, the anticipation of your teammates, your own anxiety and excitement fill your awareness with energy. You choose the latter, an inshift.

Letting go, with your attention detached, the whole scene becomes a mass of sights, sounds, feelings, thoughts that fill you with positive energy, although inside you are silent and still and in even greater control of your body. More poignantly aware of how special this moment in your life is, win or lose. Your body aims and shoots ...

You are a man or woman back in the American Wild West, a gunslinger ready for a showdown. You're nervous, your stomach churns, your throat's tight. This could go two ways.

In Scenario 1, your anxiety increases as you step out onto the street. Everyday activity—kids playing, doors slamming, people milling about—becomes an annoyance as you mentally play out what will happen in the next several minutes.

Imagining your opponent, who challenged you to this duel, makes you hate him for doing this to you. You're fretting about whether you should have spent more time practicing drawing your gun; fumbling with nervous hands, you grope to make sure your gun is there, trying not to let anyone see how scared you are.

Your opponent shows himself in the street. Fear, your internal dialogue, the people hushing themselves and watching you, all pull your attention in different directions.

How do you think you would do in that scenario? Here's the other way this could go.

In Scenario 2 you walk out into the street. You're nervous. Your mind tells you this could be it. You're not sure you're ready. Your heart pounds, waiting for your challenger to step out of any doorway at any time.

Then you channel the energy of your emotions, thinking and everything happening around you into an inner place of alertness, silent and still. Nervousness and doubt only energize you more, only serve to make you clearer, more anchored in being silent and still on the inside. Fears of dying, insecure thoughts, and images of the future are still running through your mind, but they don't stick. They don't interfere with the realization of what it is to be in this moment, the full experience of being alive right now.

That extra step, that extra knowing that you are aware of things, detaches you. It allows all the activity, noise, voices, fear, anger and dread buzzing around and within you to flow through you. It puts you in a state of even more inner silent and still energy that is and just knows. That's all you are. The whole scenario of the moment, inside and out, becomes just a full three-dimensional, real-life scenario.

The tumbleweeds tossing themselves across your horizon, the noon sun brightly shining above, the small gusts of wind that nudge you from side to side, a door slamming, onlookers murmuring comments, the internal narrator in your mind making comments about what is going on, what is going to happen next and what you should do—all of this is in the background, while the foreground is a sphere of stillness, silence, strength, energy and calm, where time seems to slow down as every moment is taken in.

Even your leg and arm movements are unique—nothing's done by rote. From this place of higher awareness, you are in more supervisory control of your body and thoughts. Your thoughts may be going in a hundred different directions, but when you need your mind to think a specific thought, it does, regardless of the rest.

You are like a flagpole that stands firm while the scene, or the flag, spins and blows in the wind and unfolds before you. Energized and calm inside, your mind and body flow evenly and spontaneously. You do what intuitively feels right each step of the way—each moment, the only moment of your life, without thoughts of past or future.

In which scenario do you stand a better chance? If you were going through life the same way, how would you fare?

17

The Process of Neural Inshifting

*If you try hard enough, you can bend the spoon;
you can shift reality.*

— *Christopher Meloni* —

The term neural inshifting comes from the word "neural," which means "nervous system," specifically the brain, and the term "inshifting," which is the experience of redirecting the stimulation of your senses, body and mind to help you pull in your focus of attention and locus of control to an inner place. There you find an inner "you" that is profoundly fulfilled and at peace.

Neural inshifting is a skill your brain already knows how to do. Naturally, millions of times throughout the day, your brain shifts in and out, from higher to lower consciousness: aware, less aware, unaware, more aware, self-aware. As we said in Part 2, it's even a significant neural inshift to wake up in the morning and recognize dreaming from being awake. The key to an incredible life is to make that skill intentional and then hone it.

Although it was adapted from mindfulness meditation, to understand what it's like to be inshifted you must get rid of your old images of meditation—of sitting in a quiet, dim room in a stuporous state of removal from the world. Inshifting involves intentionally learning to shift energy, attention and control within your brain anywhere and anytime. Being inshifted is a vibrant, attentive and portable state (meaning it doesn't require the special conditions of meditation) that leads to the relaxation and peace people ordinarily associate with meditation. The more effective your inshifting ability, the more joy, maturity, stability, and self-mastery you'll experience.

If inshifting is so natural, you may ask, why don't we all just excel at it? Why doesn't everyone just "spiritually" Awaken as a part of normal life development? In other words, why doesn't our higher brain naturally get stronger as we grow older?

Your brain does develop as you get older. You can definitely tell the biological development of the higher brain as it functions in a child and matures from a toddler to an adolescent. Yet, once you reach early adulthood, the biological development of your brain becomes less relevant than your psychological development. At that point your higher brain is able to be intentionally Awakened. Gaining wisdom, information and understanding through life experience is how we change the relationship between our higher and lower brain areas.

Some people develop their mind—their lower brain—and indirectly acquire higher brain abilities by learning wisdom, empathy and perspective. Many people develop their minds but only wind up making them more powerful. If you don't acquire wisdom, empathy and other attributes, you actually weaken the functioning of your higher brain.

A small percentage of people throughout the ages, however, have learned to strengthen their higher brain to exceptional levels usually described in religious or spiritual terms, like Awakening. These people have accessed a highly inshifted state. It has been rare for people to achieve that higher level of reality, but it is possible. It just requires learning the skill of neural inshifting, a brain regulation skill that is different from other skills in that it requires internal feedback. Yet, in many ways it is not unlike learning to dance ballet, swim the backstroke or play piano sonatas. It can be tricky to learn at first and it takes practice, but practically anyone can do it. The rewards for learning this skill are greater than for any other skill you will ever learn.

Before we go through the figures below that depict different phases of learning neural inshifting, I want to give them some perspective. Have you ever assembled furniture that came in a box? If you have, you may know that the instructions are sometimes so detailed that they make things even more confusing (some furniture companies have taken to using simple pictures, letting you figure out the details with common sense). Of course, often the instructions are invaluable, if you keep perspective and don't get mired in detail. This is the same situation here. These diagrams and the chapters that follow are meant to make a way of experiencing and a way of doing things easier to understand. Please don't miss the forest for the trees. The distinction between one step and another is arbitrary. And even though there are many things to keep track of when learning to inshift, when you finally learn to do it and begin getting better at it, you may look back and wonder why you sweated the details.

So here's the big picture: inshifting just involves discovering an inner point of reference inside your head that you are normally not aware of. Learning to experience and act from—and eventually immerse yourself in—that new inner reference point changes your experience of everything, including yourself! The inshifting steps simply help you find and maintain that inner reference and action point and they tell you what will happen as you immerse yourself in your inner eye, so you can help your transformation along. What does happen is that the world around and within you becomes more vivid, more surreal (or less absolutely real), integrated and whole, while inside you feel more alive, appreciatively amazed, powerful and spontaneously engaged with the flow of each unique moment.

Here's an overview in diagram form. Figure 8 is a "before" diagram. It shows how most people exist in their ordinary inshifted state. The larger of the middle two concentric circles represents your lower brain. Your sensory triggers, body states, mind activity, and automatic actions (SBMA) make up your lower brain. (I also refer to them as "senses-body-mind" or, if physical movements are involved, as "senses-body-mind-actions.") Without being inshifted by using reflective awareness and conscious will, your SBMA becomes a lower way of being "you." It dominates your brain and you. Your "inner eye," or "third eye," the point where you experience your higher brain (we'll call it Point X, represented by the smaller inner circle in the diagram), is overshadowed by your SBMA, keeping it small and passive and in the background of your experience of life. That smaller inner circle represents how you would actually experience the "inner eye": as a small space inside your head. It is your higher or true "you" that is reflectively aware. It knows (yes, it is an "it" because it is inside your normal sense of yourself) that it is aware, and is in a state of full conscious choice and deliberate self-direction. This diagram shows that these forces—the urges, drives and triggers of senses, body, mind and actions—mask and dominate our true selves and give us less conscious self-control.

Remember, "senses" means all five of your senses: touch, taste, smell, hearing and seeing. "Body" refers to all your drives and body states, such as hunger, fatigue, pain, restlessness and so on. The "mind" is your thoughts, analyses, ideas, beliefs, emotions, mental images, future plans and past memories. The sensations, pulls and pushes, and signals of the mind are complex and no less powerful than your body's, as anyone who has felt the emotional surge of a panic attack can tell you. Your "mind" includes the most complex, puzzling and illusory aspect because it is responsible for creating a sense of "self," the experience of an "I," which some call an "ego." "Actions" refer to automatic or rote actions, which are the vast majority. Actions like kicking your knee out in a reflex or driving a car on the freeway can all be done without higher brain guidance.

As you might have realized, there aren't really four parts to the larger circle. Your senses, body, mind and actions are all aspects of the same thing. That's why I call them the SBMA throughout this book. (I use the terms "SBMA," "lower brain," "lower you"

Before Neural- and Wellness-based Inshifting

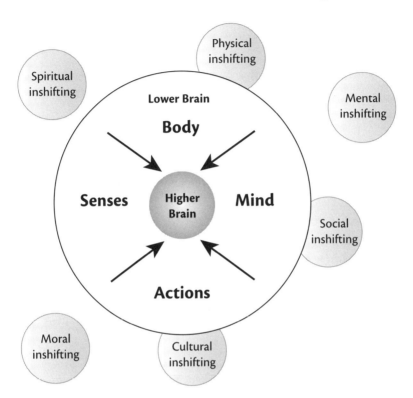

Figure 8. The situation in our brain and life before intentionally inshifting

and "outer you" synonymously.) These four aspects of SBMA overlap so much that they can be seen as one whole. For example, your *body* supplies the *senses* that your *mind* interprets. Your *mind* supplies the emotions that are felt in your *body.* Your *body* supplies the drives and urges that are accompanied by the images and goals of your *mind.* The true wholeness of your complete experience, of your SBMA, is a perception that comes with inshifting.

In this pre-inshifted diagram in Figure 8, the smaller circle is dominated by the larger one, which is the way practically everyone goes through life. It means your higher brain is not functioning to its fullest, not getting all the stimulation it needs, because your lower brain is in control. This means that awareness is passive and less reflective, an invisible witness in the back of your experience.

So that the significance of these areas is not forgotten, Figure 8 also shows smaller circles arranged in various random places around the larger two circles. Here in this pre-inshifted diagram these wellness aspects of inshifting are all shown as disjointed, uncoordinated and non-overlapping. They represent the six areas of wellness—physical, mental, social, cultural, moral and spiritual—that contain all the practices and philosophies of that area. These wellness aspects of inshifting are either a substitute for or exert a powerful influence over your intentional practice of neural inshifting. Controlled by the superficial mind-dominated, body state-controlled SBMA, you are either going to be unwell or your wellness efforts are not going to succeed.

Figure 9 shows the brain during inshifting. During inshifting the middle circle begins to open up. That means you are learning to neural inshift and the inner circle of your higher brain is expanding. As you'll see, opening up your "inner eye" (still shown as the inner circle) means learning to pay attention to that area, to put your control in it and experience from it.

As you'll learn in the following chapters, shifting in your control means finding an inner center of gravity from which you act and think. It's like someone who fights off a band of attackers using his anxious thoughts to react to their blows, as opposed to a martial arts expert who, centered within his head (his inner eye), has a calm but powerful deliberateness, seeming to spontaneously anticipate attacks from every angle.

Experiencing from an inner reference point must be experienced to be understood. It's a place inside where you think and imagine, that is more intimately you than your SBMA.

The band of the outer circle gets smaller as your senses, mind, body and actions exert less control. Also, as you learn to neural

Learning Neural- and Wellness-based Inshifting

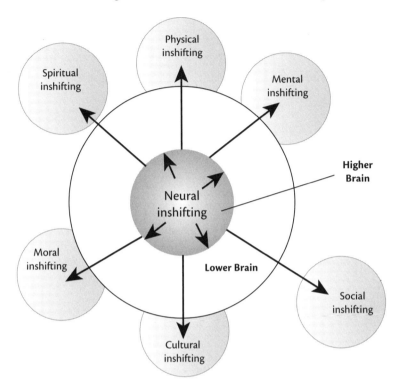

Figure 9. The brain during inshifting

inshift and use wellness-based inshifting, those wellness circles expand and get more organized. They help pull the inner circle open. If practiced with the specific goal of inshifting, the wellness areas also help you dilate that inner circle and shift in. The neural and the wellness aspects of inshifting work together: they're synergistic.

Figure 10 shows your brain after inshifting. It shows how you could exist in a significantly inshifted state, Awakened to whatever extent. The inner circle is more fully dilated, so that the "inner" or "true you" is discovered along with an Awakened reality, and the wellness circles are expanded and part of who you are.

When the power of your lower brain (the SBMA) decreases significantly and you've stimulated your higher brain enough, there is a qualitatively different type of awareness. It's an inner way of knowing, an inner self-control; an inner way of being emerges. The steps of inshifting point out how exactly that happens.

Advanced Neural-Wellness Inshifting

Figure 10. The brain after inshifting

As Figure 10 shows, when you develop yourself internally, the various areas of your life improve and help you inshift even more. The wellnesses increasingly overlap and come together as one. It stands to reason: your brain is the seat of everything you think, feel, and do, of all your interactions with people, and of your spiritual connections and life insights. It controls your immunity to disease and even how fast you age. When you learn how to maximize your brain's functioning, wellness becomes integrated into who you are, and who you are becomes your wellness. You have a healthier outlook; your body is better able to heal; you become self-confident and self-mastered, able to love deeply and widely and be loved; your life becomes ordered with passion and priorities, morally integrated and intimately connected to the universe of people, places and things; and you develop great insight into the highest nature of your reality and of yourself. You don't have to try as much to be well: you are well. The energy of your body and mind naturally cause wellness.

So, as you read on, explore, play with, and learn the exercises and skills, but don't judge your progress. It can be difficult to figure out. Sometimes in the midst of the greatest frustration comes the greatest learning. The total life wellness approach outlined in Part 5 will fill in the gaps you may have in understanding and skill.

18

The Neural Inshifting Steps:
An Overview

Every human has four endowments—self awareness,
conscience, independent will and creative imagination.
These give us the ultimate human freedom …
The power to choose, to respond, to change.

— *Stephen Covey* —

Leaving behind what you normally experience as "you," allowing and helping a new center of awareness and control to be established, you have inshifted. The experience is an inner way of knowing and acting, of being, that doesn't rely on the usual information from the senses, body states and mind activity. It's your higher brain fully directing your lower brain. Instead of your sense triggers, body states, or ideas and emotions controlling your experience and behavior, your higher brain is in firm charge when it guides and spontaneously interacts with each moment. Your higher brain exists in an open, crisp, relaxed and clear inner space that, first and foremost, knows it's alive in each unique moment.

What happens when you inshift? Usually, the combinations of your senses, body states, mind activity, and actions (SBMA) are experienced as information. A telephone ring signals a call, that rumbling stomach tells you you're hungry, anxiety tells you something bad is going to happen and you ruminate, or vice versa. This is your ordinary reality and creates the ordinary "you." It's familiar and tells you everything you have known about the world and yourself.

Instead of just serving as sources of information, when inshifted your SBMA, as they signal and interact, are also experienced as energy! The more attention you pay to your inner reference point, the more you experience things both as energy and information. It's like an inner sense organ—a sixth sense—where you *feel* the world outside and in as energy, rather than exclusively detecting information. Actually, energy *is* ultimately information when perceived from that sixth sense of your "inner eye." It's global information that you exist!

When you stop exclusively relying on specific information, you can inshift inward to become that inner reference point. In that higher reality everything is experienced both as information and from an "informationless" inner place of aliveness. Feeling how alive you are in each moment gives context to the information.

Putting attention on that inner reference point, you experience that there is no personality called "you" (there is no subjective "you"); that's another form of specific information. When fully immersed in perceiving from your inner eye, everything is experienced from a neutral or information-empty point of view. What is there is "just knowing"—a brain process that tells you that you're alive right now. The result is that without screening everything for what it can do for you, or for how to categorize and limit it, things seem more alive, continually new, energized and vivid, an independent whole that is less absolutely taken as real—a virtual brain reality, so to speak. What is there is the universal experience that everything, including you, is just interconnected energy manifesting in different forms.

As you let go of an overreliance on specific information, you can also shift your locus of control inward. That helps you let go of the struggle to directly control your SBMA. You can sense that these things are independent of you. In a higher place of control, you learn to more effectively collaborate with your sensory triggers, body, mind and conditioned actions. You become a self-director instead of a self-controller. You are the supervisor, not the micromanager, of your SBMA.

Eventually, a new "you" and a new life emerge as you Awaken into a new reality and are liberated from the programming of your lower brain.

Themes of Neural Inshifting

A few themes of inshifting must be explained because there are a lot of details to the five steps, particularly since each step has three parts. The steps are as diverse as feeling your entire body, experiencing novelty in everything and the awareness of being alive now. As I said earlier, you can get lost among the trees if you can't see the forest. The forest is the overall experience of what it is like to be neurally inshifted.

The first overall theme to finding, experiencing and acting from your inner reference point is to learn to manipulate energy. For our purposes, energy goes in two directions: in and out. "In" means that it is going into your head (Point X, your "inner eye") and used to make you more alert and stimulated and to strengthen your awareness and ability to self-manage. "Out" means that it is released, relaxing your mind and body, helping you let go and experience things with more detachment. A secret to being neurally inshifted is to learn to *do both simultaneously*—to release energy and take it in. This, as you'll see in Step 1, is a very important maneuver that you must remember to do, to facilitate both directions *at the same time*, something you are probably not accustomed to doing.

A second theme is your attention. Attention directs your awareness. Being inshifted means learning how to split your attention so that you are aware of two general areas at the same time (albeit with a change in focus): what is happening on the "outside" with your senses-body-mind-actions, and what is happening on the inside in that self-reference point that tells you you're alive each moment. (It is less complicated than it sounds.)

The other side of the attention theme is your intention—

another word for will (as in willpower). Your intention is also split, so that you can direct overall actions and thoughts while letting go of control over specific actions. That's the formula for spontaneity.

The last important theme is how you will relate to information. It's important to know, because being inshifted means to let go of your reliance on information you get from your SBMA, trusting an internal sense, a sixth sense. Again, the sixth sense you experience from your "inner eye" gives you the information that you are alive each moment. That information pierces the veil of neural illusion. It tells you what is ultimately real and what isn't: that your SBMA is a product of your brain, a virtual reality of the brain, and that the only thing you can *really* know is that you exist right now. As I mentioned before, when you experience that level of reality, what happens to your senses, body and mind as you let go of their information value is that they seem more independent, novel, vivid, and whole, and less an absolute reality. It means that the ordinary background of your experience (that you are alive each moment) moves to the foreground, and the ordinary foreground (the reality that categorizes, connects past to future, and discerns a separate you) is moved to the background. That's being fully inshifted: when you are more aware of the energy of being alive each moment than of the information provided by your SBMA, and when you are in a place of self-direction, rather than struggling to control your SBMA.

An Overview of the Five Steps

Remember, while we explore five specific steps to inshifting, they are really arbitrarily chosen phases of one encompassing skill. The important thing is not the details, but the gestalt: using energy and your eyes to find that inner reference point while you let go of lower control and a reliance on information. And as you do those things, you allow your SBMA to change, your way of being in the world to change and your experience of life to change.

Eventually, you may find that in time and with practice five steps may become three, two or even one.

Therefore, each step is composed of three themes: energy, control and awareness. You will learn to integrate them more and more with practice—lots of practice. Figure 11 summarizes the five steps, divided into their energy, control and awareness aspects.

	ENERGY	CONTROL	AWARENESS
STEP 1	Feel the energy from your senses, body, mind and action (SBMA).	Release that energy so that your body and mind are more relaxed.	Draw in that released energy so that you're stimulated inside your head.
STEP 2	Direct that energy with your eyes (oculofocus technique) to a point behind your eyes—Point Y.	Begin to let go of immediate control and reactions to your SBMA.	Begin to soften your focus on the specific information from SBMA.
STEP 3	Expand the energy behind your eyes so that you feel a stimulation in a place further in your head—Point X, your "inner eye."	Shift control to Point X inside your head, outside of your normal "you."	Use Point X to split your attention so that you *indirectly experience* the information from your senses, body, mind and actions as being detached (includes being de-identified from thoughts and disengaged from emotions).
STEP 4	Keep energizing Points Y and X.	Discover that Point X is a place of stillness where inside you feel in greater control and feel a gentle power.	Move into Point X and experience a place of openness, crisp and clear, absent of information, so that your SBMA comes together as a more independent whole that seems fresh and less absolutely real.
STEP 5	Feel an energy radiance.	Flow with spontaneous action and intuitive thought and authentic self-expression.	Know, first and foremost, the experience of being alive in each unique moment.

Figure 11. Summary of the five steps and their three main aspects

As you progress from Steps 1 through 5, each is more fully explained by the next. If you can't do any one step for long, the next one may make the previous one easier. This is why it is critical to stop yourself from trying to perfect each step before moving on to the next. Judging your performance is mind activity, information used to measure outcomes. That's definitely not helpful.

However, the steps do get more involved and removed from your normal everyday way of experiencing and doing things as you go up the ladder. Still, not to worry. Get a sense of the larger themes. And, unless you have already experienced aspects of these steps in the course of your life, realize that this is not a skill that you can expect to grasp or learn without practice. Even slightly grasping what we are talking about is enough to set in motion a positive chain of events in your brain. Insights and abilities will come when the time is right. And, once the wellness aspects of inshifting are working, neural inshifting will be much easier to learn and will happen naturally anyway.

Think of learning these steps like learning to ride a bicycle: grip the handlebars, place your feet, use correct posture, balance on the seat, don't try too hard, and so on—all things that make bicycle riding seem more complicated than it really is. The skill is tricky, but it isn't as complicated to understand and do as it may seem. The real difficulty comes from those schemata in your brain that have been ingrained by years of habit and conditioning, powerful impulses, and your addictive reliance on analyzing, thinking, imagining, wanting, planning, and defending—all things that make your lower brain so powerful that it robs you of awareness, context and the ability to self-direct.

As you progress through the steps, you'll notice that each one increasingly addresses the single most thorny yet therapeutic aspect of neural inshifting, which is the greatest obstacle you will face to peace, joy and the highest levels of psychospiritual development: your ego. Namely, each step addresses the vexing issue of how to transcend this most deeply held belief, the very notion of what you've always believed to be "you." That "you" (or ego) stems from the identification of your brain with its thoughts and beliefs. As you progress up the steps, each will face this issue in more detailed ways. To be sure, however, you can experience some degree of an inshift without fully transcending your normal self.

It is important to add at this point that for people who mistakenly believe that to transcend the ordinary "you" means to exist in a scary void, nothing could be further from the truth. Living in the ordinary "you" versus a transcendent "you" is like the difference between being self-conscious and self-awareness. What *is* scary is to live self-consciously feeling as if you are at the center of the universe (everything is about you) and, paradoxically, as if you are on the outside of life, shut out from an ideal world. Your mind, bizarrely, experiences both aspects. Think about this and you'll see that it is true. To transcend your normal "you" and become self-aware or reflectively aware is to be liberated from anxiety.

As you find your inner reference point by tackling each neural inshifting step, there is one overarching and vital tip you must keep in mind: it's got to feel at least a bit if not very enjoyable! Changing the flow of energy should feel pleasantly stimulating and relaxing, letting go of control should be freeing, detaching from reliance on information feels exhilarating, experiencing a more vibrantly connected world should let you feel more alive. In many ways it comes down to balancing effort and effortlessness. It's like learning to ride a bicycle: if you're putting in too much effort, the bicycle won't stay balanced, and riding will become stressful. With neural inshifting, there is a "zone" to each step, a place of easy effort and no force.

It takes a bit of effort to find and accentuate the solid core of alert awareness that's there inside you. But then the rest of you can relax into it. You can "take refuge" there (as a Buddhist prayer says). Relaxing, freeing, energizing and grounding should feel good. If neural inshifting doesn't feel at least a bit satisfying, you probably are straying off the mark. If it becomes stressful, you are heading in the wrong direction. That's not to say that you won't learn from going in the wrong direction occasionally. There is great value in struggling with this skill. Yet, if you don't feel a trace of enjoyment, you may be trying too hard and in the wrong way, getting tense, frustrated or discouraged, or you may not be trying enough, getting bored, sleepy or not letting go enough, all of which can contribute to the stress of your ordinary success-driven reality!

Another important point about learning the skill is that, like bicycle riding, it may be hard to master sequentially progressing through the steps in the order I present them. There are many details to riding a bicycle, but sooner or later, if you don't do them at the same time, you're going to fall. Yet, the difficulty learning to neurally inshift as with any skill is that you need to learn its steps sequentially, and probably in the order in which I present them to begin with. Down the road, you can pick and choose the sequence of steps that is easiest for you (a pattern that may evolve over time).

Also, regardless of the order in which you learn to inshift, another question is whether you should master one step before you go on to another. I think it is better to get familiar with one and then move on to the next. (Keep in mind that Steps 4 and 5 are not as much acquired directly as they are allowed to happen.) Anyway, there are many ways to learn these steps besides trying to master one at a time. Your brain may require you to first get a taste of each step separately and then try to juggle them all at the same time. Or you may just learn one step well enough that it naturally causes the others to happen by themselves. You should experiment with each one alone for a short time before deciding the best approach for you. Just remember: when balancing on a bicycle for the first time, too much effort or too little effort will cause you to fall. It takes practice to learn how to balance.

Remember, also, *never* to expect anything about this method! Don't think you will get it immediately or that you'll never be able to get it. Don't expect that the positive results you experience one day will translate to another day, that the mastery you experience will keep without practice, or that you won't quickly master it. The strategy is to not rely on your mind. Your brain is an immensely complex organ that is more complicated than your expectations. Mastery of neural inshifting cannot be measured with your mind; it has to be felt, sensed. Inner pleasure will help. Even if you are lost in thought and emotions in one session of a daily practice or struggling to inshift in a difficult situation, that may be the day that you learn the most about yourself. Your brain, without you knowing it, may learn the most about acceptance that time. You might be building potential for greater learning by your frustration or your difficulties in learning. Neural inshifting is learned, maintained and mastered over and over during a lifetime.

There are essentially two major directions to inshifting: strengthening your higher brain and letting go of your lower brain, strengthening and letting go, shifting in and releasing, taking in energy and letting out energy, and being alive each now while allowing senses-body-mind to be independent (although directed). These in-and-out dynamics are tricky to do at the same time. That's a secret to learning to neural inshift effectively—to do these two maneuvers at the same time. To help with that, I've labeled each step with the main task of taking in and letting out. Like learning to rub your belly and your head in two different directions, it only takes concentration.

19

Step 1: Energize and Release

The higher your energy level, the more efficient your body. The more efficient your body, the better you feel and the more you will use your talent to produce outstanding results.

— *Anthony Robbins* —

Step 1: Feel the stimulation value of your senses, body states, mind and actions. Relax and you'll feel that energy even more. Perceiving energy also, in turn, relaxes you. Let the feeling of energy make you more alert and relaxed. The more alert you become, the more your body and mind will relax. It's a cycle.

Everything can be felt. When you look around and identify things it is information. Yet the light that enters your eyes can be felt. Think of a time when a car headlight was aimed abruptly in your eyes and you'll immediately relate to what it's like to feel what you are looking at. It's the same phenomenon when you turn on a stereo, not knowing the volume is turned to the max. The blast is *felt* more than the music or talking is heard.

Hunger is a body state that signals that it's time to eat. Yet, when was the last time you felt hungry and really experienced the sensations of that hunger—the pure stimulation coming from your belly, the vibrations of yearning in your mouth or emotions in your chest? When you're nervous, your anxiety tells you that something has to change or be done differently or that something is wrong. But can you feel the nervousness as energy—neural stimulation in your throat, palms sweating, chest beating, even the racing thoughts you have? Even thoughts can be felt, just like sounds, if you make an effort to sense them that way.

What is information is also energy. Sensations are vibrations with different textures. Even what you're *looking* at right now—these words on the page—can be felt in your eyes. Energy is beyond words, beyond being identified as painful or pleasurable. It just is.

When you detect energy in senses-body-mind-action (SBMA), the energy stored up in those places is released. That relaxes you. At the same time you release that energy, if you draw that energy up into your head, it stimulates you.

So, we can arbitrarily distinguish three phases of this step: changing perceptions of information as energy, letting go of controlling that energy so that it is released, and drawing up that energy into your head through awareness of it. These phases of "energy, control and awareness" are mainly useful, not just because they can be experienced separately, but because they represent the same aspects in the other steps. Steps 2 through 5 also have energy, release and stimulation aspects. Again, detecting, releasing and drawing in are the sensations of energy, control and awareness. These three aspects of neural inshifting do happen on their own to an extent. They can also be helped along. So, we'll look at them separately.

Energy

Step 1 Exercise: Detecting different sensations

This warm-up exercise will help you move your aware-ness around, so that you can get ready to convert the information value of things into feeling them. See if you can switch from one texture of energy to another without moving. Give yourself two seconds in each step below to quickly feel the vibrations in the following:

- Your left hand's pinky
- Your right foot's big toe
- Your nose
- The scent of the air
- Your shoes or your bare feet
- The room temperature
- The humidity against your skin
- Your eyes: this book or anything around it
- The amount of light around you in general
- Your tongue
- The most prominent emotion in your chest or throat

Run through this exercise at least once more right now. Were you able to feel the energy in each of those?

Ready to jump into the first neural inshifting step?

Step 1 Exercise: Detecting all types of energy

Enter the realm of energy. Scan your entire body, from the tip of your head to the bottom of your feet. As if you were beaming off the Starship *Enterprise,* let the wave of sensations of your body spread downward over your face, neck, shoulders, arms, hands, chest, abdomen, back, pelvis, buttocks, legs and feet. Feel all of those sensations at the same time. Relax a bit to enhance it. Bathe in the vibrations of your body.

Include in the sensations of your body the stimulation of your body state—whether it's hungry, thirsty, sleepy, ill, in pain, sated after a meal, sexually aroused or sensual. Feel the pulsations of your heartbeat, the cool energy of your inhalation and the warm relaxation of your exhalation. Include the emotions you feel inside your face, chest, throat and abdomen. Feel the sensations of worry, sadness, exhilaration, joy or any combination without focusing on the label. Channel the gestalt of that energy into the attentiveness in your head.

Now open up the energy bath to include all your senses. Feel in your eyes what you see. Do not discriminate in what you see, just experience vision. Do the same with the sounds around you. Feel them in your ears without making distinctions. Let the air temperature stimulate, the smells permeate, the pressure of the chair or ground beneath you press on you. Sense all that information as energy. Bathe in the flow of all that energy at the same time.

The last sensations are the most subtle, the closest to you and the hardest to experience as energy: your thoughts, the images in your head and memory, even your beliefs! This is master-level awareness that converts information to energy. The other steps are geared more toward helping with this, but try it now anyway. See if you can feel the activity in your mind. Feel your inner voice as you would a sound. Sense the images in your head as you would a sight. Be aware of the activity of your thoughts as a source of a subtle swimming sensation in your head.

Control

When you feel all that energy, it'll start to be released. You can feel energy exiting as relaxation.

Step 1 Exercise: Release and relaxation

Try to feel energy from your senses, inside your body, in your mind and in your movements. To whatever extent, as you let this energy go, you'll feel a heaviness to your muscles, a lightness to your senses, a distancing of your mind, and a decrease in action. Allow the experience of those sensations to calm you. Help it along a bit. Take control by allowing it to go, by not holding on to it. Don't be afraid of losing control. You're increasing control. Just feel the tingling surge as it exits.

Awareness

The more you are aware of energy and its release the more it can stimulate you inside your head. Awareness draws the energy up as well as releases it. You can help that along to make you more alert, to feel vibrant and enlivened while relaxed and slowed.

Step 1 Exercise: Feel the stimulation

Relax your face a bit and draw up into your head that energy you converted and liberated. Let the energy detected and released from senses, body, mind and action begin to stimulate you. Feel the tingling of that stimulation. Let it make you more alert, awake, up, aware.

Energy is beyond good or bad, or identification. It just is. Remember, the experience of energy is pleasurable. If this doesn't feel pleasurable, you're probably forcing it.

Arousal energy is the energy your brain uses to function. Remember, the energy of arousal is a specific type of energy that has its own tracts of nerve cells that run the length of the brain stem into the brain. Called the Reticular Activating System (RAS), these tracts are branches off the main tracts from the spinal cord that are en route to convey information to your brain and use those nerve impulses solely to stimulate the brain. The arousal energy and RAS function to get you up in the morning. When you're tired and ready to sleep, arousal energy is turned down.

A lack of energy in your head can feel like depression. Too much unnatural energy can overwhelm your ability to channel and release it, like you've had too much coffee. When energy is too high and uncontrolled in your *lower brain,* your arousal feels like restlessness, impatience, tension or agitation, where you just can't settle down, or it feels like anxiety or irritability. That kind of arousal energy can be exhausting. Exhaustion from agitation is the opposite of relaxation and stimulation. If energy gets out of your control and you can't channel it into alertness and calm vigilance, your emotions and thoughts can spin out of control, and restless legs can really get moving.

There is a shortcut to increasing arousal energy that you can play with at some point. It's a *temporary* maneuver to increase energy in your higher brain, especially if you are getting tired. It can easily work against you, becoming a distraction and lending control to your mind activity (not what you want) if you try too hard or too long. The trick is to magnify the energy in your head with your mind. Think about how actors raise their own energy level before going on stage. They gear themselves up or pump themselves up for the performance to take on a different role in front of crowds. They channel anxiety into alertness. Soldiers do this when they snap to attention during an important inspection. Athletes can get themselves "psyched up" right before a contest. Again, this trick can work for only so long. Don't rely on it.

If you are really tired, you should follow the recommendations in the physical wellness chapter to find ways of naturally increasing your energy. Those practices, as well as those that help relax you, are tremendously beneficial for Step 1.

People who take a stimulant medication to slow a hyperactive or inattentive brain are doing the same thing you are in Step 1, but with chemicals. The energy of the stimulant causes their higher brain to be activated, ideally more than their lower brain! Energy channeled to the higher brain helps it fulfill its chief role: to inhibit the lower brain. That allows you to relax, settle down, stay alert and be in much greater control.

20

Step 2: Grounding and Loosening

*Awareness requires a rupture with the world we take
for granted; then old categories of experience are
called into question and revised.*

— *Shoshana Zuboff* —

Step 2: Your eyes are the hands of your brain. Narrow the
channel of energy into your head with your eyes into a
place behind your eyes. This gives grounding, focus and
stability to inshifting. Use that concentrated energy to
begin softening your focus of attention on any one thing
and loosening your direct control over any one action.

In Step 1 you got a sense of what it is to experience energy
instead of just information. Step 2 will help you ground and
stabilize that ability by narrowing and drawing in that energy behind your eyes. That moves your point of reference inward by releasing your reliance on information and need for direct control.

Energy

The experience of converting, releasing and drawing in energy in
Step 1 can be difficult to sustain. It's one thing to bathe in the
feeling of energy. It's another thing to do that for a period of time
unless you're coordinating it from a single location. Like a one-

way channel with a one-way valve, you eyes can be used for this purpose. They can also draw in that energy and keep it continually flowing inward. The first way station for the energy is in the back of your eyes, a spot I call Point Y.

That spot strengthens you. It changes the places from which you pay attention to and control things. It moves your *focus of attention* and your *locus of control* further inward to a place more centered behind your eyes. Moving in your attention and control can be made easier with a maneuver I call oculofocus (ŏcŭlo-focus): "ocu," for ocular, is the use of your eyes, and "lofocus" combines the words "locus" and "focus." "Locus" refers to the point of control, and "focus" to the reference point from which you experience things (see Figure 12).

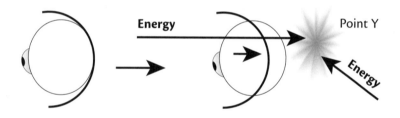

Figure 12. The oculofocus technique

In this technique, your eyes are used as guides to gently pull your *attention* and *intention* (your will, so to speak) inward. Very slightly, gently and comfortably you actually pull back your eyeballs, without straining them, so that you seem to be experiencing things and controlling yourself from that spot inside your head. It should really be a light and easy move, making you as nimble as a professional dancer or as agile as the kung fu fighter anticipating his opponent's next move.

Using the oculofocus technique is not a visual maneuver. It involves softening your eye muscles, so it doesn't matter whether your eyes are open or closed, or whether you are looking at anything in particular. You are simply using your eyes to pull your attention and control inward. You can still see normally.

Point Y is the entry point, the beginning edge of what Hindus early on recognized as an "inner" or "third" eye. They believe this is a spiritual energy point or energy "chakra," located behind the forehead between the eyes, from which you can view a spiritual reality. Step 2 begins the process of discovering the fuller extent of that "inner eye."

The oculofocus can be a prop to concentrate your energy and give you more strength and power. The effect of the energy can be a bit like mild-mannered Clark Kent peeling off his street clothes to become Superman. His whole demeanor changes: he becomes confident and powerful. What we're talking about is not usually that dramatic, although some people could feel a dramatic revitalization if their energy is usually low, or they feel exhausted, slumped over and defeated by life. It can be a strategy to reenergize.

The area behind your eyes does become a new center of gravity, grounding, stability, and intentional control and power. Power here does not mean force! It is a gentle power seen in gentle men and women who are strong inside, grounded, but peaceful in their countenance. It's a flowing power you'd see with a martial arts expert who uses his or her opponent's strength against them.

Step 2 Exercise: Energy

Bathed in energy, awake and relaxed from Step 1, experience that energy from behind your eyes in Point Y. Feel the energy being drawn into your head. Use the oculofocus maneuver to direct energy in with your eyes, into the back of your eyes. Use Point Y as a sense organ. Feel it vibrate with stimulation from everywhere. Remember the Superman analogy: let it strengthen, stabilize and ground you. Let it vitalize you even more than you felt in Step 1.

Control

You've energized and drawn in energy behind your eyes. Now there are two releasing aspects to this step: loosening direct control over and softening the focus of attention on your senses, body state, mind and activity (SBMA). Now we'll help loosen your locus of control. It means to find enough inner strength to let go of the forceful and direct control of your body and mind. So if you are buttoning your shirt, loosening your locus control means that you stop trying to button your shirt so hard and allow it to be buttoned by your lower brain. The difference between automatically and mindlessly buttoning a shirt and consciously releasing your hands to button it is like night and day. It is the difference between being on autopilot and being spontaneous. One is unconscious and the other deliberate.

Loosening control releases your natural talents. If you were playing the drums, you would stop trying so hard to keep a beat and allow your sense of rhythm to play itself out. Loosening control is also inhibiting. While going through the checkout line in a supermarket you would be better able to pass by all the magazines and candy put there to stimulate last-minute impulse buying. Loosening control allows you to let go of self-consciously controlling thoughts and word formation so that you can have a more authentic conversation. The strength you derive from your eyes and Point Y can give you the strength to start loosening your immediate and direct control over the triggers of your SBMA.

Here's another example of what it means to force direct and immediate control over your sensory triggers. Imagine waiting impatiently for a red traffic light to turn green, ready to step on the pedal. If you've ever been in that situation, you know that if the car next to you lurches forward first (or the left-turn arrow you weren't expecting turns green when you aren't turning left), you can easily react reflexively and step on the gas pedal in a quick false-start.

You can even react strongly to a stimulus you weren't at all expecting. Say you hear a sudden scream from another room. You jump up in confusion and either charge in there ready to overreact or run in the other direction, assuming the worst.

Those reactions are mind-body reactions, not actions from a higher awareness and self-directed control. The same is true for exerting tight control over your body states. For example, say you quickly get a stomachache, or any pain for that matter. Most people will automatically try to push it away by clenching their muscles to resist it. It's an instinctual reaction. They don't want to feel the pain. Yet, it's a reaction that doesn't work in the long run. In many cases muscle contraction and anxiety make pain worse or even unbearable.

Similarly, overcontrolling your mind, just like overcontrolling your senses and body states, is not the best solution. Trying to control your emotions directly by fighting feelings such as depression, or trying to stop unacceptable thoughts by pushing them out, doesn't work and makes them come back more strongly. Say you're trying to find the courage to ask someone for a date. Forcing yourself to be brave and to think positively or imagine positive results has limited effectiveness. We'll see this more clearly in the higher steps of neural inshifting when you learn to self-direct instead of control.

Again, forcing actions also doesn't work as well. For instance, while learning to play the piano, you can concentrate so intently on what your fingers are doing that you struggle to read the notes. If you over-control your movements when learning to play the piano, you can get in your own way, as any professional can tell you.

Don't worry, though. As you let go of trying to control your SBMA, you aren't going to completely lose control, mess up, go crazy or become humiliated. That's what most people think, so they struggle to keep control, to fake being happy or to fight their impulses. That detachment from tight self-control transforms into more self-direction.

Transferring control to higher brain regions after years of using lower ones can feel scary. Giving up a dependence on keeping everything in check and in tight control is a risk. You have to give up ideas of perfection or an ideal way of being and doing. As you replace micro-management with macro-management or executive control, you'll see (Step 4) much better control and effectiveness.

Step 2 Exercise: Loosening control

Try this: as you strengthen yourself by energizing the back of your eyes, use that strength in your eyes to let go. Just as you released energy in Step 1 and felt relaxed, feel the release of letting go of the need to react. Remember, energizing Point Y keeps you vigilant and grounded, better able to monitor your SBMA. Loosening control, you feel yourself relaxed in a different way. No urgency. There's patience. Readiness to act. Allowing things to unfold (like the traffic light) before action. Allowing things to unfold (like piano playing) while acting. Suspending judgment before believing. Accepting emotions before reacting to them.

Awareness

When you draw the energy of your world inward to the area behind your eyes, use that energy to soften the focus of your attention. Softening your attention means to not fix your *mind* on any single thing. You can experience sights, sounds, body sensations, thoughts, feelings and so on without letting your concentration rest anywhere, without identifying anything. That includes naming, classifying, recognizing, distinguishing, singling out, acknowledging, understanding and so on. Just experience the whole scene.

You may not realize it, but every time you recognize anything or are aware of any single thing, odds are that you are thinking about it. When you think about something that you are experiencing or that you are doing, the thought focuses your attention and controls you and who you are. As you learn to control your mind (and SBMA), you learn to control your attention. One way to control your attention is to soften it so that it doesn't focus on any one thing to the exclusion of anything else! By softening, you stop relying on thinking.

Here's an example of softening. You might, for instance, look at a chair sitting in a room. Instead of zeroing in on the chair so that everything else around it, including what you can see or hear or think, is blocked out, do this. When you soften your attention, you can still see the object, but you see it in relation to what you see around it, or to other aspects in the moment, such as the whole room, the air temperature or your feelings. The softer your focus of attention, the more your awareness takes in. As we'll see in Step 4, the more your awareness takes in, the more every moment turns into a whole, a gestalt.

A gestalt is a whole. It is like looking at the picture of the jigsaw puzzle instead of a collection of individual pieces. The definition of a gestalt is that the whole is greater than the sum of its parts. With enough practice at softening your attention, your experiential gestalt can widen so much that everything becomes one big experience—the world and you with it. It has been said that, upon Awakening, one can experience the universe, all of one's reality, in that one thing.

You can think of a softening of attention as similar to classical versus impressionist paintings. The Renaissance paintings of Michelangelo created a detailed scene that required you to look at part of the painting and focus on each aspect separately. Now think of the impressionistic paintings of Monet. They *keep* you from paying attention to any one thing, so that you attend to the gestalt of the scene—the entire canvas. In a softened experience of life, you can still be aware of individual things, but (as you'll see in Step 5) you don't lose the context of the moment.

Softening your attention prepares you for the next three steps. Part of Step 3 is to move from softening to detachment (of attention, as well as de-identification with an idea of you, and disengagement from emotional connection). It also prepares you for Step 5, part of which is to just know first and foremost that you're alive while directing your mind and body to act and interact with things and events. Softening your attention enables your attention to move inward, to an inner place and way of being. That's the objective of neural inshifting.

In case you're wondering how you could possibly go through life not concentrating on single items, you must realize, first of all, that softening attention is the start of increasing awareness that you'll see in later steps. Think of the opposite situation: focusing your mind on one thing to the exclusion of everything else is part of how you can get hypnotized. Instead of being in the gestalt or the totality of the moment, your mind, fixated on something, steals your attention and limits your awareness. Ultimately a state of mind called dissociation happens, where your awareness is severely constricted and limited, even though you happen to be awake.

So to know how it is possible to go through life softened, or even detached, from specific elements of your experience is to complete the steps. You'll see that your *mind* can focus on specifics, that you can pay attention to one aspect of your SBMA, while your awareness is open, detached, present and encompassing.

Step 2 Exercise: Softening attention

Use your eyes and the strength that gives you to relax your attention. Pull in your attention so that it doesn't rest anywhere in particular. No force is required. This uses a gentle oculofocus maneuver of softening your eye muscles. Hear everything but nothing in particular. See as much as is naturally around you, but not any one thing. If you can, think whatever comes into your mind, feel whatever comes into your awareness, but don't rest your attention anywhere. Include body sensations and emotions that may come up as well. Just like the "letting go" that you did in the last exercise, rest nowhere but in the back of your eyes. Allow yourself to be aware of the energy of everything. You're drawing in energy to your eyes from everything, and not settling on any information associated with it. Ultimately the experience of the energy of each moment and the experience of labels or information in each moment can live side by side.

Step 2 Exercise: All together

Feel the energy of your inner and outer surroundings stimulate the back of your eyes: Point Y. Oculofocus, pulling in your eyes slightly, so that the energy is drawn behind your eyes. Again, soften your eye muscles a bit so you can direct your attention to soften. View the moment you are in without letting your mind fixate on any one thing to the exclusion of anything else. See how experiencing the vibrations in your senses, body and mind automatically softens your focus.

Loosen your direct control over your senses, body and mind. See if, like riding a bucking horse, you can ride their impulses and automatic movement, even if, like buttoning your shirt, you are doing things that seem intentional. Energizing Point Y while softening and loosening should feel good: grounded, exhilarating, relieving. Point Y is a place of peace and energy no matter what happens and no matter what you are doing. Stay conscious of your actions and flow with your brain as it is drawn from one sensory pull to the next, from one thought and feeling to the next, from one body state to another.

If you hear a loud noise, stay centered in Point Y. Quickly feel it as energy instead of trying to figure out what it is and where it came from. When you have a brilliant thought or feel a feeling, be aware of the energetic aspects of your mind activity. Allow yourself to experience the energy of the thoughts or feelings as well as what they tell you, so that you more fully experience them and they pass fully through you. In this practice, there is no need to push away thoughts and feelings or to try to block out sensory stimulation.

Remember, like each step, Step 2 should feel enjoyable and pleasurable.

I discovered a fun use for this aspect of neural inshifting that should make this skill well worth learning. I was playing a video arcade driving game one day. Focused on my hands steering and on my mind coaching me how to drive a virtual car at high speeds on an obstacle course, I realized wasn't performing at my best. I was anxious about not doing my best. The anxiety, coaching and separate focus on my hands and feet were all making me overcorrect my steering and drive in spurts of wild speed and hard braking. My thoughts were literally driving the situation.

Then I remembered neural inshifting. I grounded myself with my eyes. It allowed me to let go of direct control, of trying too hard. From an inner place or locus of control, grounding and energy, I allowed myself to drive in a more relaxed fashion. I softened my focus of awareness and felt the energy of the moment: the sounds of the room, the feel of my body sitting in the seat of the video game, the coaching, and my hands, feet and mind doing the virtual driving. Observing my mind taking in the information from the video screen and my body automatically adjusting was a singular experience. It was much more enjoyable, and I was doing better! My score was increasing really fast, right up until I started thinking of how cool it was to drive better.

21

Step 3: Splitting and Detaching

To study the Buddha's way is to study the self;
To study the self is to transcend the self.
To transcend the self is to be enlightened by all things.
To be enlightened by all things is to remove the barrier
between self and others.

— *Zen Buddhist Master Dogen* —

Step 3: From Point Y you move energy, attention and control further inward to your inner reference point. It's a place that is perceived as if it is in the center of your head. It's where you normally think and imagine—but inside even those functions. We'll call it Point X. When you move energy and attention there, you'll experience the higher control that lets you let go of lower (direct) control. You'll experience the sensation of it being apart from or inside the normal "you." It's an inner "you" where you can experience being aware indirectly. It's where you are fully alert, but detached from your senses, body and mind, freeing you up for higher awareness and freedom.

In Step 1 you felt energy in and around you. It energized you inside and relaxed you. In Step 2 you concentrated that energy behind your eyes using the oculofocus technique, loosening your control and softening your attention.

Now, in Step 3, you will embark on a maneuver that may seem strange and foreign at first. It will take you out of the realm of how you usually control things and yourself and how you usually experience things and yourself. It is the step that lets you begin discovering a new inner way of being you.

The exercise in Step 3 is to access an inner spot we'll call Point X. It's an area deeper inside your head, in the same place where you normally imagine things and think—except even further in! It's inside, separate from the normal you that you've come to be familiar with and that you've relied on. The ordinary you is the way you usually control and experience your senses, body states, mind and actions (SBMA).

Energy

Step 3 involves energizing that inner spot we've called Point X.

Step 3 Exercise: Expanding inner energy

From the grounding and concentrated energy of Point Y, you can draw that energy farther in. Let the general feeling of stimulation in your head from Step 1 now be concentrated in a more compact space inside your head. It's an ill-defined space, roughly the size of an orange, that stretches from the back of your eyes to the back of your head, from the roof of your mouth to your forehead. Let it be permeated with cool, fresh, vibrant energy—again, without forcing it.

Point Y was the first step. It's the traffic cop directing energy inward. Use the oculofocus technique to help feel the energy in your head. See how it automatically draws your attention to Point X. Let the stimulation of that area relax and enliven you. Let it calm your thinking. Let it be pleasurable.

Control

Point X is an inner place of control. In the following steps you'll experience more of the strength and gentle power of this inner place. In Step 3 the first phase of that strength and power lies in letting go. Remember, in Step 2 you loosened direct control over your SBMA using Point Y, the area in back of your eyes. Here, you'll do the same thing, although you'll use the area called Point X—the one we have talked about as being farther in your head. That area feels (at least at first) as if it is apart from or inside you.

Remember the scenarios of the person bathing, the basketball player and the gunslinger? To Awaken a bit, think of how they gave up direct control of their performance expectations, anxiety about dying or need to grip onto and heighten an already wonderful experience. This step is about continuing the process of letting go.

Think of a martial artist. Where does he find the strength to break wood and bricks? He has to let go of the fear that he can't do it! How is he able to fight two opponents at the same time (or a really fast one)? He begins by letting go of his fear, of automatic impulses to blink or duck, of ideas about winning, or of anger toward his opponents. Point Y was the beginning of this process; Point X is the peak.

Point X is deeper inside your experience of the world and yourself. It penetrates more core aspects of your mind. It contains the very essence of who you are. The more you let go of control, the more you'll feel a higher, inner power that is more grounded, mature and gently powerful.

As we mentioned in Step 2, letting go of direct control may be hard to understand at first. It largely entails inhibiting impulses. To let go of your senses you find Point X and use the strength of that area to not reflexively react, without awareness. So you would inhibit the impulse to, say, physically jump or mentally jump to conclusions with every loud, unusual or even routine noise that comes into your brain. Ditto for changes in scenery, itching sensations on your skin, sudden announcements over a loudspeaker, the smell of smoke and so on.

Letting go of body states means keeping from reacting impulsively to hunger by running to the refrigerator or not allowing the sight of sexy bodies walking to a beach distract you from driving. Letting go of mind means inhibiting the intense impulse to call someone you recently broke up with, just because the thought flashed through your head, at least not until you've had time to think it through and get in touch with your higher intuition.

Letting go of automatic actions means that when you are learning to play tennis, you resist the impulse to hit the ball when it's still too high in the air after it bounces, before it has a chance to drop to waist height. It means to wait until you have a more intuitive certainty about timing before you blurt out something in a meeting.

Inhibiting actions and reactions needs the inner strength that comes from energizing Point X. Feeling the energy within Point X is the way to access more of your higher brain. It must be energized and accessed so you can stop your lower brain from its automatic actions and reactions. This helps you let go and learn to release and relax. Inhibiting is not usually a matter of exerting force. It also means feeling the triggers of an automatic action so fully that you don't react.

In Step 1 feeling energy energized you inside and relaxed you outside. Experiencing energy stimulates and strengthens you within Point X and settles your lower brain. When your mind quiets down, when your impulses are not so keyed up and your body states are not so intense, that is much of what it means to let go. Letting go, when there is time to consider your actions, also involves making a choice to let things go, to wait and to consider.

Step 3 Exercise: Letting go of direct control

Energize your head. Feel Point X. Feel its inner strength. Experience how it is apart from how you're feeling, what you're thinking, or who you feel like you are. Experience that point of control as deeper in than your senses, body states, thoughts, feelings and actions. It's a different, more in-control side of you.

Feel how the intensity of that energy actually settles you and strengthens you at the same time. Watch how your body and mind relax as you take more charge inside. Notice how you move less, but more deliberately, how the pointless activity of your mind quiets. Witness how your movements become more intentional and your thoughts more deliberate, just by relaxing. Observe how energizing Point X grounds you and puts you in greater control.

Awareness

When I say Point X is outside (or inside or even other than) the normal you, what do I mean by that?

Just like we spoke about in Part 2, The Realities of You, there is an ordinary you and an Awakened you, an ordinary way of being and an inshifted (eventually more Awakened) way of being. The ordinary "you" comes from your lower brain, and, in particular, your mind. It dominates your higher brain. To understand how experiencing Point X can help you leave your ordinary self and find a higher Awakened self, let's briefly talk about how you experience your mind.

When you think about being aware of your own mind, think about those annoying songs that get stuck in your head. That's one way you can objectively recognize the workings of your mind. There are also inappropriate thoughts, including mean-spirited judgments about people that pop into your mind that you would not speak out loud.

There is the part of your mind that most people can't see (probably including you), because they are so close to it they experience it as "them." For instance, your identity as "David" or "Elizabeth" and your individual "camera angle" on the world are experienced as taken-for-granted aspects of you. That's the normal "you." When I say that Point X is inside your normal "you," that's what I'm referring to. Here are more examples.

You think to "yourself" about things, right? You narrate your life to "yourself," occasionally criticize "yourself" and try to convince "yourself" to do things. Basically, you experience the world largely along with this talking "self." When you mistake that "talking self" as you, it means your lower brain is in control of you and is talking to that silent inner "you." It's your lower brain overcontrolling outcomes. When that narrator part of your mind drives what you do and think and experience, it means the real you is a totally passive witness to your life (even though your mind and body are active). Accessing Point X begins the process of making that passive witness active.

So there is a split. On one side is the outer, normal, ordinary or everyday "you." It's projected from the lower brain that speaks, understands, has ideas and believes in things. In particular it (your mind) believes its identity and that it is in control of what you do. It has goals and expectations, connects to your history, interprets the world and its events, and reacts.

Then there is the higher-brain "you." Again, it is usually passively aware of what your lower brain is thinking and doing. This is arguably the oddest aspect of owning a human brain: it can be split between two radically different ways of being aware.

To continue with neural inshifting you must split your attention! That's the awareness aspect of Step 3. Here's how you can accomplish that split in your attention between the lower you and the higher you: learn the skill of *indirect awareness*. Here's what I mean.

Have you ever had an eye examination? There is a part where the doctor looks directly at you and tells you to stare straight ahead at her nose. Then she places her fingers to the left and right side of your vision and wiggles them. You can see her fingers, even though you aren't looking directly at them. This is how you see things out of the "corner of your eye" without looking at them directly.

Step 3 Exercise: "The wriggle technique" of indirect awareness

Try this kind of medical examination for yourself. Stare at one spot and wiggle your own fingers to the sides of your eyes. You can see them indirectly, without looking directly at them, right? Now, gradually move your fingers to the center of your vision, but keep staring straight ahead. Without locking your attention on them see if you can still see them, even though they are right in front of your face! If you can do this, you are looking at them with detachment (or "indirectly"). You see your fingers, but your eyes don't lock focus on them. It's just a continuation of the softening of attention and loosening of control that we explored in Step 2.

In this same way you can hear things, sense things on your skin, experience your emotions, and think and act, all with indirect or detached awareness. "Mindfulness" has been called "awareness detached from experience." This is what that means.

Here is another analogy. Imagine walking inside a conference hall when the lights suddenly go out and it's pitch black. You might stop walking, but after a short while you will adapt and keep walking using an internal sense of awareness. That's because you have shifted your locus of attention inward from using your vision to Point X, which is aware of your senses, body states and mind all at the same time. It's an inner eye, a detached way of knowing objects and ideas, inside images and moods, and your senses. *You can only experience things in this indirect way if you are experiencing from within Point X.*

Step 3 Exercise: Generalizing indirect awareness

See if you can feel Point X. Now, just as you practiced the wriggle technique where you had the experience of looking at your fingers wriggling in front of you without locking your attention on them, look around the room you're in. See it as if you can experience what it is like to see the area where you are with that same strategy. Look around, but don't let your eyes lock on any one thing or adjust to see what you are looking at.

Now try it with your hearing and the sense of your body and your face, in particular. Then try to be aware of what you are thinking and feeling emotionally with that same indirect detachment.

See if you can notice (if you are not forcing this) how centering and energizing this feels. Notice where the majority of your attention is. If it isn't "out there" hooked into your beliefs, thoughts and feelings, it must be "in here," centered inside, in Point X.

You can, of course, still identify things when you are indirectly aware. You still know what's going on: what you are seeing, hearing, feeling in your body and detecting in your thinking and emotions. You still know your fingers are wriggling in front of you. What is happening is that you are feeling your senses, body and mind *more* by having detached or indirect awareness. It lets you experience them from a different center. It's an inner locus of control and focus of awareness centered at Point X.

What does this aspect of Step 3 practically do for you as you move through the course of everyday life? It alters the *situations* in your life. "Situations" are moments when "you," the subject, interact in some "event," "story" or "plot," with something inanimate or animate. You can even interact with your own mind. Your mind arranges it so that your life is a string of situations. When you can experience situations both indirectly as just mind phenomena and directly as a real story with information, you stay grounded and objective. You cannot get lost in over-identifying with anything or anyone. That's totally freeing—putting you, not circumstances, in control.

DE-IDENTIFICATION AND DISENGAGEMENT

There are different aspects of detachment. This has to do with the uniqueness of your human mind. Detachment from your mind is being "de-identified." As we said, you de-identify by letting go of personalizing or projecting yourself into some situation, person, place or thing.

You identify with other people when you let them define you. You identify with situations like your dreams when you believe they are true, or with a hallucinogenic drug trip or psychotic delusion if you think they are real, and if you have automatic thoughts and jump to conclusions based on them. That's a way of identifying with your own automatic thoughts. You identify with things. When you experience life situations by locking your attention into them, you experience everything as either yours or not yours, about you or not about you, and so on. That limited way of being in the world is shallow and inaccurate and sets you up to overpersonalize the situations in your life.

Identification with aspects of your mind usually happens subtly. It is part of your normal existence. When you believe anything as an absolute reality, beyond just knowing you are alive, you are identifying with it. De-identifying is a way to let go and find freedom.

Disengagement is another way of saying de-identification, except the focus is on your emotions instead of your thoughts. To disengage is to find a place of neutrality relative to your emotions, objectivity in the midst of subjectivity. It is a way of letting go of the powerful control your feelings have, without changing them in any way!

Being attached to your senses, body and mind, identified and engaged, is so much part of our lives that we don't even know we are doing it. You must constantly let go of the plot, the drama or story of each moment so that you can find, in the energy of the moment, that inner place of detached awareness.

THE OBSERVING EGO

The benefit of splitting your attention in Step 3 is that you can feel the energy of a situation with indirect awareness while you interpret it in your mind as an event. It takes practice and is a bit tricky, like learning a new dance while talking to your partner at the same time. It's mastered gradually.

Experiencing from Point X is what psychoanalytic theorists (followers of psychiatrist Sigmund Freud) would call the "observing ego." According to psychologist Richard Niolon, PhD, "The observing ego is the part of us that watches what we do or say in some objective manner." Further, the observing ego "watches all this and tolerates the anxiety that is produced." This is the therapeutic benefit of being able to let go and observe indirectly so you can better tolerate discomfort. Raising your tolerance for discomfort is remarkably freeing. It means you run less from boredom, loneliness, embarrassment or pain. You're less likely to make rash or unconscious choices. In Buddhist circles the observing ego is called the "silent witness."

ACCEPTANCE AND SURRENDER

Letting go and indirect awareness require acceptance and often surrender.

The opposite of acceptance is wanting to change things. When you want to change things, you want to try to make them better, to possess, reject, capture them with your mind and label them, to be part of, seek to distance yourself from, or even hang on to them and keep them from changing.

Experiencing the energy of things helps you accept them. You can't feel the energy of something and change it at the same time. You have to accept it.

In case you are concerned that accepting reality as it is means that you have to like what your lower brain interprets as horrible or that you have to let "horrible" or "painful" things happen without trying to stop them, let me relieve your fears. Accepting the reality of something as it is happening, fully feeling it, lets you understand it better. Experiencing energy and information gives you an advantage in understanding the information. When information is based on fuller experience, it puts you in charge. It keeps you from blindly reacting. It puts you in a much better position to do something effective. You act more intelligently and spontaneously, as opposed to reflexively, when you aren't selectively screening information. Your mind is likely to deny that something bad is happening before it accepts it. Your mind is also likely to be programmed to try to automatically change a situation without a full firsthand experience of it.

As the writer Henry David Thoreau said, "Nothing can be changed until it is faced." Acceptance is the prerequisite for change. Acceptance and surrender are time-honored spiritual practices. According to author Eckhart Tolle, "Not until you surrender does [the spiritual reality] become a living reality in your life... Through surrender, spiritual energy comes into this world... It is a silent but intense presence that dissolves the unconscious patterns of the mind" (Tolle, 1999).

THE BEGINNINGS OF A "SPIRITUAL" EXPERIENCE

Does Step 3 of neural inshifting explain more about what Eckhart Tolle is describing? Indirect awareness or detached experiencing cause you to accept events and things the way they are unfolding. As we'll see in Steps 4 and 5, regardless of what you do with that information it allows you to be in the clear openness of the moment. That's the hidden so-called spiritual reality. Detaching attention, de-identifying who you are, and disengaging automatic emotions put you in a state of Now. Experiencing information alone forces you to discriminate. Information often becomes a signal of pain or pleasure, survival or death. It induces you to competition or capitulation. Acceptance and surrender move you beyond those distinctions. It puts you "in the world but not of the world." When you accept things the way they are, you are one with them, as they represent the entirety of being fully in each moment. Looking at your wiggling fingers with detachment, you are accepting them the way they are. Surrender to the reality of them the way they are.

22
Step 4: Openness and Power

Meditation is the dissolution of thoughts
in Eternal awareness or Pure consciousness
without objectification, knowing without thinking,
merging finitude in infinity.

— *Voltaire* —

Step 4: Experiencing indirectly allows you to turn your attention inward. Become Point X, a place of clearness, openness and crisp emptiness, where there is no information from senses, body states or mind. That means no goals, time, expectations, stress ... no you. Relative to that inner openness, everything else is perceived as more whole, independently flowing, vivid and less real. Having let go of direct control, Point X becomes a place of higher power.

In your very essence, who or what are you? Every neural inshifting step takes you closer to a more complete picture of what you are. You are not the image you see in the mirror, nor are you the identity you have grown up with or the reactions people have to you. You aren't your body, or its hunger, headache or restlessness. You aren't even the anxiety, sadness, restlessness or dissatisfaction of your mind. You aren't that intimate narrator that keeps you company all day, or even the very idea of "you."

Strictly speaking, you aren't even a "who," you're a "what"!

You're a process of reflective awareness—a brain that has mechanisms so sophisticated it can know that it exists. *What* you are—this process of reflective awareness of your higher brain—is *housed* or experienced within Point X. Experiencing from this inner reference point, you'll find yourself in an inner place of clear openness. In other words, Point X is a place of "silence and stillness," the experience of several things that it does not contain! Sometimes referred to in Buddhist texts as "sunyata, which means infinite emptiness and radiant openness" (Surya Das, 1997).

Filled with energy, your higher brain takes over more as the site of your experience. Yet, your higher brain is not set up to receive specific information. (Remember, from Part 3, it is involved in multimodal sensory integration, the kind of information that solely tells you that you are experiencing.) As a result, when you are experiencing from that inner space that represents your higher brain, the experience is absent sense, body or mind information—relative to all the SBMA information and specific images buzzing around! It's sightless, painless, itchless and deaf. No thoughts, emotions, stress, goals or even time! It's a clear and empty reference point (besides the awareness that's there), again, relative to everything else.

Stress, goals, senses, time, mind, body—these are just signals, energy waves from your senses, body and mind that convey information. Turning them into energy transforms them into something enlivening and real yet empty and clear. For example, information from the experience of time, experienced as change, doesn't exist in your higher brain, because your higher brain doesn't need time to do its job and know it exists. That's a lower brain perception. Time helps the mind learn about and navigate life. Neither is there the necessity for an image or experience of "I am" in Point X. It's egoless, no narrator, no idea of you.

In essence, learning to experience things/information *indirectly* will cause you to more *directly* experience and then *become* this higher reality we've been talking about, the reality spiritually attuned people have been talking about for centuries. It starts with experiencing from a place of silent and still emptiness. That's what it takes to have inner serenity and strength.

In other words, relative to the information and movement experienced by your lower brain the "true you" is an inner blank reference point that witnesses. Keep in mind that the terms "witness" or "observer" can be misleading because they conjure up a "who" that is witnessing. What you will experience is a process of witnessing or observing. It's an "it" not a "who."

What does directly experiencing (and eventually becoming) a silent and still reference point do to the experience of everything that is processed by your lower brain? It changes it! What you used to take for granted is seen in a new light. Things, sights, sounds, ideas, sensations seem new, fresh and interesting. Experience becomes more of a totality. The elements of your awareness are taken as less real. You experience them more as your own brain images, a virtual brain reality.

Steps 4 and 5 have a somewhat different quality than Steps 1, 2 and 3. Like a full-on Awakening itself, Steps 4 and 5 are less about what you do to achieve them than how you allow them to happen. This is an important point to bear in mind.

Energy

The strategy in Step 4 is to continue to infuse Point X with energy, as you did in Step 3. By this stage you're going to really feel the glow of that energy.

Control

Part 3 explored the brain science hypotheses of neural inshifting. Part of that was showing how your lower brain is able to function on its own with very little, if any, awareness and guidance from your higher brain. Your lower brain has an incredible intelligence. It's like a robot that can do everything, in a basic way, including think and solve problems. In Step 4 you'll begin to experience that intelligence more.

In Steps 2 and 3 we practiced letting go of controlling that intelligence because that gave you more strength and power. What I didn't say was that the more you let go, the stronger you get on the inside. Now you'll learn how to really experience that control. It's like riding a horse.

The horse is like your lower brain—a fairly intelligent, physically powerful beast. The rider is like your higher brain. When your higher brain is passive and underused, it's like having a weak rider. Either the horse will do what it wants and the rider is helpless or the rider struggles to overpower the horse with force because he is ineffective. He doesn't have the true power that it takes to really be in control instead of struggling for it.

Let's practice riding our horse.

Step 4 Exercise: Higher control

This is a standing and walking exercise. First, inshift:

- Feel the energy in your SBMA, release it and let it stimulate your head.

- Transfer control to your eyes and concentrate energy behind your eyes (at Point Y), soften your attention and ease up direct control.

- Concentrate that energy farther into your head (at Point X), so that you are able to detach your attention (indirect awareness), experience a split ("you" versus it) and more fully let go of control.

Now, stand up intentionally and smoothly, with deliberate intent for every movement (as if doing a tai chi exercise—a Chinese form of martial arts that develops mind and body by having participants move through a series of stances in a slow, methodical, smooth and intentional manner).

With this level of intentionality experience your body as a separate, powerful and responsive beast. You are the invisible gentle power that directs its movements from a detached vantage point—like watching yourself button a shirt, initiate the motions and guide them, but let go of direct control. Synchronize your body's breath with its movements. Move the body forward, one intentional footstep after another. Feel the changing pressures on each foot as, intentionally walking, it steps to the ground. Feel the balance and elevation of the airborne leg. Slowly move around the room in a circle, aware of energy, indirectly aware of what the beast is doing and in what environment. Relax and feel the ease of control.

In this manner, your SBMA is respected and treated as an independent source of intelligence, one that must be directed rather than forced. This way of being and doing works in any situation in life. It allows you to carefully work your mind and eyes to watch the movement of a tennis ball on the courts so that you can hit it at the perfect height. (This is as opposed to solely thinking your way into a tennis game by imagining some ideal of what it means to play tennis.) This way of mentally controlling yourself allows you to wait before you pass judgment on a belief you have about someone until you achieve a better understanding of them. These are all benefits of increased self-control.

This inner wisdom and control reminds me of a part of the Alcoholics Anonymous Serenity Prayer, which Bill W quotes in *AA Comes of Age*: "grant us the serenity to accept the things we cannot change, courage to change the things we can."

Awareness

Here is an example of what it might feel like to discover a place of silence and stillness within you.

Step 4 Exercise: The birthday party!

Imagine you are about to enter a room full of children at a birthday party. You can hear it before you go in, but as you enter you are abruptly hit by the sounds, smells, temperature and activity: howling and screaming kids are throwing paper, jumping on chairs and running in circles. Almost overwhelmed, you wince and recoil from the confusion and turmoil, ready to make a quick exit. Then you see an adult you recognize across the room. She acknowledges you with a broad smile and seems to be open to and enjoying the commotion. Interesting. You suddenly see that for her this is part of what it means for children to celebrate. She gets pleasure from the kids' noise.

You reconsider this moment and experience it a different way. You relax and stop trying to avoid the experience, instead feeling the energy of the moment. You stop shrinking from the commotion. You allow in the sounds, sights and movements as energy while you detach from it, enjoying it as a celebratory whole, momentary experience, a din of information and stimulation experienced in its entirety *from an inner place of quiet.* You acknowledge the other adult—one person in a place of silence and stillness to another person in a place of silence and stillness. Again, it's quiet and still in your head only *relative* to all the noise and activity that you see, hear and feel.

If you focus inward, you can experience that inner place. Detached and de-identified from outer reality, fully accepting of it, you'll find a "silent and still" openness within you. With practice, you can experience everything from that place of clean, fresh luminousness.

When you enter more fully into silence and stillness, it becomes more than a *place*. It is more than silence and stillness "within" you. You *are* that place. You *become* that place. There is a big difference between trying to *find* a place of silence and stillness and *being* a place of silence and stillness.

As you learn to inshift, it will feel as if you are splitting your attention between the silent and still energy in your inner eye and the indirect experience of the things in your ordinary life. It is as if you were at the birthday celebration, experiencing the noise and commotion from a place of silence but recognizing, "I am in a place of silence." As you progress, there is no special state to recognize, no "I" to observe the emptiness! You *are* the place that is silent and still. Spontaneously flowing in that place, it is no longer an *inner* place. It is you.

DISCOVERING A NEW WORLD

What happens to all the information in this state of silent or clear witnessing? What happens to all the activity in your senses, body, mind and life?

It gets more vivid—evidencing its energetic properties. It appears fresh and novel—indicative of the uniqueness of each moment. It gets more unreal—showcasing the piercing perception that all we really experience is our own brain. It becomes more of an intelligent, interconnected whole—religiously described as evidence of "God's plan."

Normally, your senses seem stable and absolute, like gravity. Trees are always trees. They don't melt like ice. Your body is always right side up, not upside down. The room is always still.

Spin around, though, and stop, and the room will keep spinning without you. Walk on an escalator that isn't moving and you'll feel like you are actually moving. Take a hallucinogenic drug that warps your perceptions (not recommended, just imagine it) and you will experience your senses in ways you never imagined. The world of your senses is not as stable and real as it seems.

Likewise, your mind seems stable and absolute, but it isn't. What draws and disgusts you, how you see yourself and your life, its past and your place in it, can seem unchangeable. Yet people in exceptional circumstances change in ways they would have never predicted. Think about people who've had an Awakening-like epiphany after a serious car accident. People trapped in elevators during blackouts connect with each other in ways they never would have before. Similarly, body states seem unchangeable, yet during a fast, once you overcome the psychological hunger that drives most of your meals, physical hunger tells you what it really means to be hungry. It can also paradoxically feel good to feel deep physical hunger, just like it can feel good to be able to cry when you're sad.

With a different way of experiencing, everything can seem different and new, more vivid and enlivening. With the global information you get from experiencing energy over the tired habits of perceiving specific information over and over, a new way of seeing can make you come alive anew. Each moment represents new energy patterns, which are forever changing, instead of seeing a chair as a chair over and over. Not that your senses, or even your mind and body, have changed in any way, nor has your sensory system been modified. It is just that how you experience makes everything novel. It makes things stand out as "signal" that would previously have been "noise."

Unreality

A new way of seeing unmasks the ultimate illusion: that you are experiencing anything other than your own nervous system! Step

4 lowers the veil of illusion, what Albert Einstein called "the optical illusion of consciousness." Like putting on a virtual reality helmet or taking a trip on the holodeck of the Starship *Enterprise*, having an empty and clear reference point shows the unreality created by your lower brain. In other words, when your focus of attention comes from a place farther in your head, it's like going behind the curtain of a theater and seeing all the illusions of the stage. This goes hand-in-hand with experiencing novelty; they're different sides of the same phenomenon.

What importance, you may ask, could this possibly have to my development, to my mental and physical wellness, and to Awakening? Seeing past the illusion created by your nervous system through inshifting helps you Awaken to a more fundamental reality. It tells you that true and foundational reality is inside you, and that everything else is impermanent and as changeable as your brain chemistry is after eating sugar or drinking alcohol. That perception is reassuring and grounding, and helps you see through and resist the unhealthy aspects of society and the games that people play.

Your mind is subjective, biased towards your personal viewpoint, but your higher brain is objective and experiences without biases and viewpoints. When you know that you are experiencing your own brain, it makes you more objective. You can control for the subjectivity of your mind. You can experience the same inshifted reality as anyone else. So in this sense, an inshifted, Awakened spiritual reality is a universal reality that everyone can share.

Everything is changing and will always change. Only your lower brain stages a production that features a universe that can be captured and identified, that can remain static. That has you believe deep down that you and your existence will last forever. An empty reference point that knows it's a brain teaches you to take nothing for granted. It's a powerful lesson.

A Gestalt

Remember the exercise about the children's birthday party? The whole buzzing commotion of the event came together as you inshifted into a deeper place of silence and stillness. No longer discriminating as much, such as between what is good or bad, likeable and unlikeable, useful or non-useful, the universe that includes you emerges as a whole. It's a gestalt.

A gestalt is a term for a way of experiencing a unified perspective, whether it's a whole painting as opposed to individual figures in it, or someone's whole humanity as opposed to aspects of their personality you dislike or admire. A gestalt is defined as a whole that is greater than the sum of its parts. This is important to your life because it connects you to something greater than an individual you.

As you shift in your attention so far that you have an open reference point, you'll experience the reality created as your SBMA comes together as a gestalt. That gestalt takes on meaning that it wouldn't otherwise have. Merely focusing on one part, one concept, one philosophy, one dimension, you miss the interconnected energy that surrounds and pervades you. You neglect a firsthand understanding of the nature of our interconnected universe. Feeling and knowing that you are connected to the whole, to everyone and everything, is a very powerful insight.

As far as the inner openness of Point X is concerned, you might be thinking to yourself, why in the world would anyone ever want to go grocery shopping, talk on the phone or drive to work in a place of openness? It seems so artificial and weird.

(Of course, it's weird only until you are used to it.) The answer is precisely because this way of seeing gives you an experience of connectedness regardless of what you are doing, an experience of unreality that gives you wisdom, wonder and insight, and the objectivity to be mature, to empathize and to fairly witness yourself and others. Openness in seeing keeps you from getting caught up in your drives, in information that signals pain or pleasure, in stress, in time and in yourself so that you can better appreciate being in the moment. Open and clear experiencing gives you greater self-direction powers when you can witness your seemingly irresistible impulses to eat junk food late at night. When you talk to your kids from a place of detached awareness, you can appreciate them in this moment, their true developmental level, more than your ideas and expectations of them and how kids should act, which allows you to act toward them with compassion and wisdom.

Openness gives you a fascination for the newness of what was formerly tedious, boring or invisible to you. The grocery store can be seen for how it's laid out, how its employees are trained, how the fluorescent lighting makes you feel. Openness transforms the annoyance you may feel with your parents when they try to control you into gentle appreciation. It makes the journey in your car part of the destination. Openness helps you proceed through your life guiding and directing instead of controlling and struggling.

23

Step 5: Just Knowing,
Spontaneously Flowing

Is it me? Is it me, Me, Me, Me, Me? It has to be me—
but is it!? It is a question a thief must ask himself
the night he jimmies open his first window, and
it is said to be the question with which
bridegrooms quiz themselves before the altar.

— Philip Roth —

Step 5: Inside the openness of silence and stillness lies the "true" or "inner" you—the aspect of you that feels most alive in each moment. Turn your attention more pointedly inward and you'll be aware of the brain process of reflective awareness that tells you that you are alive. Knowing on a deep level what it means to exist each unique and precious moment, reflective knowing is a dawning realization of the significance of your life, offering a profound sense of context for the moment and your entire life and a sense of an "immediacy nostalgia." This insight comes with a different kind of control: flowing and spontaneous self-directed action and rapid synthesis of logic and intuition, all of which makes you a highly authentic person.

Congratulations! You've reached the last step in neural inshifting. By now you've discovered that individual elements of each step are understandable and, it is hoped, doable—yet can take some practice. Are you wondering how you can keep all of what you've learned together? Do you get the feeling that another step may put you over the edge of what you can hold together in one skill?

I still feel like that at times. Then I remind myself to relax into each step and feel pleasure; to stop using my thoughts to judge and force the steps and to feel them instead; and, when I've reminded myself of them all, to keep going from Steps 1 to 5 without stopping to perfect any one, because Step 5 can bring them all together.

Right from Step 1, when you transformed your experience into energy, you began entering that psychospiritual realm. Each step widens that realm for you. Now in Step 5, in the midst of this wondrous emptiness and spaciousness you uncovered in Step 4, you'll find within you what some have referred to as the "divine," Universal Mind or Buddha nature itself. Why? Because that clear openness energy, as we've said, serves as a unique kind of information. It's an ineffable knowledge and insight into the core of your existence, the soul of your being.

That's reflective awareness. And although reflective awareness is your brain reflecting on itself, that experience encompasses the universe that is in and around you. You'll find the essence of the universe mirrored within you. In this entryway to "heaven within" life becomes easier. It flows with intuitive understanding and spontaneous action.

Energy

There is a slight but real difference in Step 5 from the previous steps. The more you allow your brain to transfer energy, control and attention to your higher brain the more a feed-forward process can happen. It amounts to a snowball effect. At a certain point, when you've learned what it feels like to be reflectively aware, you will not have to intentionally shift energy to Point X. Energy will flow there naturally. It happens because when your brain's internal mechanisms are reset, your higher brain areas are used more readily, so energy will be drawn there automatically.

In religious literature it's been noted that this energy snowball effect looks like someone has a radiance to them. When your higher brain is stoked with energy, things can seem to glow. In Step 5, however, there's nothing explicit you need to do in the realm of energy. It just happens.

Control

INNER CONTROL TO THE POINT OF SPONTANEITY AND AUTHENTICITY

Step 5 Exercise: Reacting spontaneously

Imagine that you've been asked to speak to a large group of people on a complex subject you are not familiar with. There will be dignitaries and other people personally important to you in the audience.

You walk out to the podium as the auditorium hushes and quiets. As you begin to speak, you turn around to point at the screen behind you, and people begin to snicker. Your confusion just has more people laughing more loudly. You look down around you to find a long sheet of toilet paper stuck to your shoe and leading all the way off stage.

You're not inshifted, but you know how. You very quickly go through each step.

- You feel the moment: the sight and sounds of the audience, the intensity of your embarrassment and the tension in your body. You're enlivened instead of constricted, and it instantly relaxes you.

- Your eyes ground you. You begin loosening control, which means you show your emotions more. Your embarrassment increases a bit along with a feeling of sadness. You begin paying attention to the whole situation, instead of just your embarrassment and the laughter.

- You shift the energy of those feelings to Point X and begin letting go of the informational values of your feelings even more. The energy in Point X helps you become increasingly indirectly aware of everything going on. It detaches you. The situation becomes less personal.

- In a matter of seconds, there is an opening up within you, a clarity. You feel stronger, protected. The situation and your embarrassment seem more weird and unlikely. The irony of your fervent desire to look competent and the unlikeliness of this bizarre event strikes you as humorous.

- It seems really funny. How ridiculous. You begin laughing, too, in a spontaneously authentic way. It feels like the audience is joining you: you are connected with them in the absurdity of this moment. You rip the toilet paper from your shoe, still laughing. Then you immediately settle down and return to what you were saying from the point where you left off. The audience is left to follow your lead and quickly get back on task.

Greater and greater self-control naturally leads you to be spontaneous in what you do and in how you think and express your emotions. You become less an actor and more the real you.

Inshifting to the point of detached awareness lets you master the art of supervising and self-direction instead of struggling to gain self-control. But that's only the beginning. Choice becomes spontaneous when it mingles two sources: logic and intuition.

SPONTANEOUS LOGIC, INTUITION AND CREATIVITY

Logic is explicit. Your thinking can be spelled out on a blackboard. One step rationally leads to another.

Intuition is implicit, unknowable. It relies on brain processing that is unconscious and happens on many levels. It's a gut instinct. Your brain analyzes emotional impressions and accumulated knowledge in the context of its unique recorded experiences. It cannot be trusted alone to make decisions. Yet, when balanced with logic, you have your best chance for wisdom and for successfully negotiating life.

Spontaneity is the ability to allow both types of processes for you to make a decision. When you have inshifted, you can readily, or at least more readily, discern the right combination of pure logic and pure intuition for any given situation.

Imagine, for example, that you are sitting in a restaurant. You have a moderate weight problem and had planned in advance to skip dessert this night. You're having a wonderful time with great friends and haven't felt this happy and relaxed for almost a year! The waiter then announces that they have an exceptional dessert made by a well-known guest chef.

Should you have dessert? Inshifted, the answer might come quickly and easily, or it might take a while. The result would be a decision that feels very right, whether it's to splurge this one night, stick to the plan, or split the dessert with a friend. In an inshifted state, you would be able to fully immerse yourself in the process, combine the best of logic, intuition and creativity, and come up with a decision that you can fully get behind!

Because spontaneous choosing feels very right, it's different from having your senses, body and mind compete for whatever pulls you the most strongly or to have them aligned but without the guidance of higher awareness that gives context.

Spontaneous action frees up your body and mind to perform at their best because of the energy generated by your higher awareness and its ability to oversee but not force or over-manage. After you learn something, spontaneous control lets it unfold on its own. It's a natural result of getting out of the way and letting go. When you play the piano after much practice, it's spontaneity that makes the difference between a gifted performer and a technician. It is the ability to deliberately get out of the way of your body's and mind's training.

The same thing holds for the ability to immediately restrain yourself or act. Spontaneity is the ability of your higher brain to freely inhibit behavior that is out of accord with your logical and intuitive self-interest. Seasoned martial artists, who seem to others to "react" instinctively, are mainly inhibiting their impulse to react. Spontaneity needs higher awareness. Conversely, the highest levels of awareness are more easily achieved when you approach neural inshifting with a degree of easy spontaneity.

This last aspect of spontaneity is fun, satisfying and very useful: creativity. Many scientists and inventors who've made significant discoveries say that the moment of creativity that sparked their idea didn't come to them when they were consciously trying. It happened when they had been thinking about a solution and then focused on something else. The idea then popped into their head. Inshifting seems a useful tool to enhance your creativity. If you think about a problem, then inshift long enough, your brain will be freed up to synthesize the information and come up with an innovative solution. This goes along with perceiving novelty in Step 4.

Step 5 Exercise: Spontaneous walking

Open up your inner eye, inshift and walk around a room. See if you can do it with self-direction instead of rigid self-control. Direct your mind to know where it wants to go. Then direct your legs to take you there. Smoothly stay aware of your walking. Float instead of bang around. Try to deliberately stay out of the way of your body.

You've undoubtedly been spontaneous before. Remember those times? You were feeling good, energized and relaxed, able to just be yourself without worrying about what anyone thought of you. That vibrant energy can get channeled into your daily life so that everything flows better. Work on being yourself. Inshift so that you can enjoy the flow of just being you. Learn to trust yourself.

Awareness

You might ask: if inside the inner sanctum of my experience is clear and empty, how does that make me a unique being? Who am I? Or what am I? The question can also be phrased as: how does my inner self that is silent and still, filled with energy and indirectly experiencing, make me, me?

The answer is that what makes you, you, is the same function that makes you a sentient being, a conscious entity: reflective awareness. Remember it's the function of your brain that tells you (without words), "There is existence. I am part of it."

In some ways reflective awareness is just another brain process, the mechanism of a body organ. Yet there is nothing more crucial to your quality of being! There is nothing as special, amazing or complex in the known universe! It's the pinnacle of biological evolution. It is the peak of universal evolution, the universe becoming so complex that it can look back on itself. And yet it has no personality or thought or subjectivity. That all comes from the lower brain.

The realization of reflective awareness comes by pulling your attention sharply in.

Step 5 Exercise: Reflection

Stop what you are doing. Take a few moments to sense what it's like to be aware this moment. Turn your attention inward to do it. It's not out there. It's a "pulled-in-here" awareness. Experience existence. It's distinct from anything you can know with your senses, body or mind. You've experienced this to varying degrees throughout your life, such as in very private moments when something special or exceptional has happened. It draws you into the moment as if to say, "It's me ... that's really here."

If that is too difficult, use your mind with its ability to appreciate. Try to appreciate what it *means*, how incredible it is that you are aware right now. You're alive and that's not going to last! This isn't a movie that goes on and on. It's happening. Each second is precious and unique and will not be repeated! Let the clouds part and try to experience "now." Grasping that improbability lets your mind back you into the experience of this level of reflective awareness.

USING YOUR MIND TO FIND YOURSELF

Using your mind to create a direct experience ultimately doesn't work. It *is* possible to use your thoughts as a tool to help you temporarily teach yourself how to experience indirectly while directing part of your attention much closer in. However, the trick is to then quickly let go of thinking and switch into an experiential mode so you don't start a habit of mistaking thoughts and imagination for real experience. Given those warnings, here are thought exercises to help you reflect on and appreciate your awareness. Ideally, they will give you a better gut or experiential sense of what it means to more fully experience your aliveness.

Step 5 Exercise: Appreciating existence in vision

Imagine that you have been blind your entire life. A new surgical procedure has just been performed, the bandages have been removed, and it allows you to see for the first time ever. What is it like right now? Are you immediately focusing on *things* or on the *fact* of your vision? Where is the *experience of having vision*: out there or in here somewhere? Where in here? Can you feel amazement that your eyes work? Are you discriminating between what is beautiful and ugly, or are you drinking it all in?

In a few years or even months, what are the chances that you will be taking your vision for granted the way you take your awareness for granted now?

Step 5 Exercise: Appreciating existence in changing landscapes

Imagine you lived your entire life on a desolate rocky landscape. Having been instantly teleported to Manhattan you are driving in a convertible with the top down. The wind is blowing in your hair, fumes are in your nose, and there are canyons of skyscrapers, throngs of people and noisy commotion. Where is your attention in these first seconds? It is probably on the stimulation of the experience, on what it is like to be alive in this moment, which you sense inside you.

Can you imagine how the extraordinary sights and sounds and smells and temperatures of the city can be one whole, panoramic, vivid and unreal landscape of "a city" experience?

Step 5 Exercise: Appreciating existence in acquiring sentience

Imagine you are a lifeless robot with a highly advanced computer chip just inserted in your head (like Data on *Star Trek*). The chip gives you instant awareness. (And, of course, the ability to reflect on that awareness, or you couldn't do these exercises.) Can you get the intensity of an inner realization of being alive? Can you get what it means to experience a neural reality?

Step 5 Exercise: Knowing awareness in recognizing your brain

Here's the most relevant exercise of all. How do you know you have a heart? If you listen or feel it carefully, you can feel its beat in your chest. How do you know you have lungs? You can feel the air expand your chest and rush past your nostrils. How do you know your eyes work? You see things right now.

How do you know you have a brain? Can you experience it right now? Where or how can you experience it? Can you detect that *it* is thinking right now? Is it moving your muscles right now? Is it experiencing sounds, sights and touch right now? Is it awake right now? Is it aware right now? Is it experiencing being you right now?

How is it that you are able to know all that? Can you experience yourself as just a mechanism of that organ?

Experiencing your aliveness is one way you experience the brain you exist in. It's how you can tell your brain is programmed with the illusion it is a "someone" rather than what it really is: an impersonal organ. That experience is not a rude awakening. It is a joyful and fascinating coming home to Truth. It is freedom from your same old ways of experiencing the world and you with it.

Remember that reflective awareness means to "know that you know something," which is different from just "knowing something." Knowing something means you are aware of things like talking to people and could recall what happened throughout the day if you tried. "Knowing that you know" means that you are aware of the act of being aware of something at that moment. That kind of knowing happens inside your head, without words or images. It really is the experience of being right here, right now—a never-ending sense of "now." It's the intangible realization of what it is like to be in the moment. It's when you are aware of the aliveness of the moment, not just *what* is happening.

It's not self-consciousness. That's when you feel awkward, as if you are the center of uncomfortable attention. Reflective awareness is being more attuned at times when you are extra aware of taking in the moment. It's enlivening and spiritually Awakening.

There are at least three ways you can increase reflective awareness. The first is to neural inshift. The second is to realize your aliveness, using your imagination to guide you. The third is to experience being a brain rather than a personalized someone. Each is found by loosening your attention from being stuck "outward." You find it within inner silence and stillness.

Step 5 Exercise: Reflective awareness

Inshift. Feel energy from things, release it and draw it in. Oculofocus and concentrate the energy behind your eyes, using your eyes to soften your focus of attention and relax control. Expand to Point X farther in your head with more stimulation, to the degree that your awareness becomes detached. In that state of indirect awareness (unfocused attention) feel an inner openness. Oculofocus even more, so that within that openness you can sense the experience of "aliveness now." Can you feel the intangible awareness of being in this moment? Do you experience the energy of being alive from deeper inside?

This way of "knowing" is your essence. It is your true nature. Like a pebble dropped into the center of a pond there are many ripple effects to the experience of reflective awareness. Here are a few.

The ROYAL Now

ROYAL is an acronym for Realization of Your Aliveness. It was meant to have a double meaning: first to experience reflective awareness by realizing your aliveness, and second to show the majesty of becoming acutely aware of the meaning of your existence.

We spoke about "realizing your aliveness" in the thought exercises, where you imagined being a robot that is suddenly actually alive. It is a facet of "knowing that you are aware," but what does it mean to realize your aliveness? Don't we already know we're alive? On some level, of course we do. Yet the intense firsthand experience of it is taken utterly and completely for granted. We can't see it because it's too obvious, like water to a fish, so we don't appreciate our existence nearly as much as we could. That's a wondrous and magnificent fact—that we exist. It is the jumping-off point to an Awakening, the cornerstone of a level of reality that brings us the deepest meaning and highest bliss.

There is a majesty, a royalty, to that awareness. It's the realization that each moment of your life has *tremendous significance*. Each moment is as important as each thought, action and choice of royalty, important leaders, famous scientists or celebrities.

When you watch a documentary on the life of a famous person, you are interested in the decisions and experiences that determined the directions of their lives. In that sense your life is like a *living* documentary. Each moment of your life, even a seemingly mundane one, is significant when you realize that the fact that you are alive is an extremely rare and miraculous thing and that your preciously short life is never going to repeat itself.

The problem with the acronym is that the word "your" says that there is a "you" to realize aliveness. However, to really be in that place of emptiness of ego there is simply "realization of aliveness," not the idea of you realizing aliveness. It may seem like a small difference, but it's significant enough to make the term technically incorrect. Regardless, the acronym is useful to remind you that you are as important as any person on Earth.

Context

If you have walked contemplatively along the ocean shore, you most likely have experienced context, as you have in tragic or in special times, when you're aware of your whole life in relation to the passing moment. When you're at a wedding, the significance of the moment brings your entire life into view. When your house is burning down, having context tells you that this is a moment within a sea of moments in life. Part of context is realizing that "this too shall pass."

A ROYAL Now is close to the experience of context. Realizing the royal significance of each precious second leads to perspective, to the "big picture." Context is experiencing the individual object in relation to the whole. It happens when you loosen your focus of attention outward and bring it inward.

Context is therapeutic. It gives you wisdom, so when your children are pushing your buttons, you can realize they are just children and that this is part of childhood. Context gives insight into people and situations. It gives maturity. It leads to an appreciation of being alive.

However, most of the time we don't have context. Gripping onto the things in your experience leaves you narrow-minded, reactive and suggestible. You can be more easily manipulated by others and even by your own explanations when you focus on something to the exclusion of its background. That's because without context you lose boundaries. You identify yourself with it and it controls you. Context gives self-control and self-insight.

Immediacy Nostalgia

Closely related to a ROYAL Now and context is "immediacy nostalgia." Nostalgia is a harkening back, a wistful reminiscence of days gone by, the good old days. Even if those good old days were not perfect, people still miss them because they realize that those "wild and precious" days were once-in-a-lifetime days and aren't coming back. Particularly if you have children or had a great love affair you will look back in time and miss these days. If you are wise, you expect to be nostalgic someday in the future.

Reflective awareness, the ROYAL moment, and context all contribute to "immediacy nostalgia." It may be hard to realize what it means to be nostalgic for something that is happening now. That realization was taught to me by a friend. She had unexpectedly dropped over, and I was complaining about how frustrating and embarrassing it is to have a constant mess in the house because of my children. She said, "Someday you'll miss the mess." It was an epiphany. "Someday," I repeated to myself, as I saw it in my mind's eye, "I *will* miss all this." It awakened an appreciation of that moment, and I felt nostalgic for everything that was happening.

The fact that you are alive and getting a chance to witness your life unfolding is immediacy nostalgia, a direct result of surrendering to the moment. Even as we try to change events (or clean our house), we can still appreciate the struggle, because we are witnessing events from an inner locus of peace and perspective.

24
Neural Inshifting: Summing Up

From within or from behind, a light shines
through us upon things, and makes us aware
that we are nothing, but the light is all.

— *Ralph Waldo Emerson* —

Again, there are not five steps or 15 substeps to inshifting, there is only one skill. It is one maneuver that can be quickly accessed with enough practice. It doesn't need to happen in discrete steps. Like playing tennis, it's just one swing with different aspects, but it's a unified experience.

The five steps I've outlined are inclusive. If you have reflective awareness, you'll be perceiving energy, you'll have a level of calm alertness, you'll use your eyes, you'll be letting go of control and trusting in a higher mechanism of control, you'll experience "awareness detached from experience" and things will seem constantly newer, more whole and less absolute. Once again, these steps could have been arranged in many ways and you can use them for many purposes.

Keep in mind, there are many obstacles to neural inshifting. Remember to try to mitigate some of them to make neural inshifting easier for you. Some examples are as follows:

- Being blocked from arousal by excessive fatigue or illness
- Being overly stimulated by drugs or uncontained emotions
- Being lax
- Perfectionism or trying too hard

- Fear of letting go or lack of trust in the process
- Not experiencing a degree of pleasure at every step
- Grasping for pleasure

The wellness chapters will help you with the many other challenges you may find as you begin the ROYAL journey of neural inshifting.

Questions and Answers

Q *The steps seem so complicated—energizing, relaxing, loosening, softening, inner stillness, outer vividness, knowing you know, spontaneity—it seems overwhelming. Can't it be easier? Is there one technique that can at least get me started?*

A Yes, there is! If you're finding the steps overwhelming, then just start by being aware of your entire body, all at the same time, from your toes to the top of your head. Keep your entire body in awareness without settling your attention on any one part. Do this while you are sitting, walking around, talking, writing and so on. Practice this strategy regularly, five to ten minutes at least three times a day, and whenever else you think of it—while driving, eating, playing video games.

Keeping this type of awareness is relatively easy. When you find that you are good at it, you can further enhance it with all the steps of inshifting. Gradually that body awareness will include the other senses and your actions and reactions.

Q *That total body awareness skill should help. Yet doing the rest of the inshifting steps seems daunting. Is it ever really possible to learn to inshift effectively?*

A   Don't be discouraged. Remember, the steps that I presented are *not the only way* you will learn to inshift. The most
obvious example is in the chapter on traditionally spiritual
inshifting, where we explore formal ways to neural inshift,
including a meditation practice, and techniques and tricks
that make inshifting easier. These include creating a specific
time to do nothing but practice, enhancing your posture or
counting your breaths to keep you in a state of detached
awareness or reflective presence.

The chapter on physical wellness inshifting teaches
methods to help you be naturally alert and tranquil. The
chapter on mental aspects of inshifting offers insight into
your personality so you can inshift from it. All of the wellness-based inshifting chapters have techniques and practices
that can help you recognize and better manage mind, body
and life. That's the point and the beauty of having both para-
digms in this one book.

Q   *Can you review the various ways to find Point X?*

A   Here are seven.

- Draw energy into your head by softening your eyes and
  directing it inwards.

- Experience everything indirectly (with detachment, de-
  identified and disengaged). You will be viewing it from
  Point X.

- Find an inner place of silence and stillness amid noise
  and activity. You will be experiencing from Point X.

- Experience where Now is. It comes from being immersed
  inside your head in Point X—not out there.

- Experience where you feel most alive. Right, Point X.

- Balance on one leg. You will better find your balance
  when you are centered in Point X.

- Breathe in through your nostrils. The cool air coming in over your palate can stimulate Point X.

Q *Should I start at the first step and progress through each one at a time?*

A To start with, yes. However, as soon as you are familiar with the steps, then start wherever it feels most comfortable to you. Sometimes I start with feeling Point X and detach, then stabilize it with my eyes. At other times I start by experiencing my body as one whole. You will vary depending on where you are in learning the skill. Remember, there aren't separate steps. They were presented to explain the overall skill.

Q *Why do you distinguish between my brain and me?*

A I sometimes use the word "it" rather than "you" because your brain is so powerfully attached to your mind and body. "It" tells you that your core, the part that is silent and still and just knows, is a brain mechanism. "It" reminds you that there is no "you" deeper inside. The experience of you is ultimately a process of reflective awareness.

When you can recognize "who" you are as really being a function of your brain, it automatically helps free your brain from the grip of its mind. Remember, the brain is a body organ, silent and still, but aware. There are many transmitter chemicals being triggered by chemical electricity beaming down the length of nerve cells. There isn't any light in there, and there aren't any sounds or mental images that can be picked up by any scan. There's no you.

Q *If I have a functioning higher brain, why do I need to do anything to make it work better? Doesn't it come fully functional?*

A No. Modern society is a severe challenge to natural higher development, and your brain needs to be developed. The strength of your mind, the might of body drives and the power of human society to program you can weaken pathways to your higher brain. In any case, just like any skill, mastering the skill of inshifting requires instruction and encouragement.

Q *Is the purpose of neural inshifting to avoid stress? Isn't some stress good for you, making you stronger? Is it even practical to think you can go through life without stress?*

A Life provides ample opportunities for stress: crises, commotion, excitement, even intense pain and pleasure. It is good and arguably more important to be able to inshift during those times to minimize stress. So if you practice your skill when the conditions are ideal, such as in a quiet room, or in situations you anticipate will be stressful, such as an interview, you'll be better equipped to do it when you need it in extreme times. You could be in the middle of a war zone, freaked out and reacting to every gunshot and explosion, when you realize you can take care of yourself by finding that inner place of silence and stillness. Remember, *stress is not so much what happens to you as how you react to it!*

    With all that said, we should be very careful about how we understand inshifting in relation to stress. Your body and mind can be greatly "stressed," but the inner you doesn't need to be. That you can be an unstressed silent and still witness of your own stress is a strange idea, to be sure. Body, mind and outside events will be stressful, but that doesn't mean you have to be stressed to your core. This is a tricky concept. You can be in an inner place where there is no stress while your body and mind are highly stressed and outside circumstances are stressful. To be ultimately in an inner place of no stress means that even though your mind might be feeling miserable or anxious, or the worst imaginable thing has happened, you can experience it all from a place of acceptance, where it is okay, because existing is better than not existing.

The goal of life is not to never stress, but to find meaning in your existence, bringing you and everyone satisfaction, leaving the world better because of your existence. Stress is part of living, but it can be transformed into energy and enjoyed on a deeper level.

Q *In my ordinary day-to-day life am I not using my higher brain? It sure seems like I'm in control and aware. How can you use just a little bit of your higher brain? If it's functioning, doesn't it function fully?*

A It is extremely difficult to comprehend how the "you" that you've always known is not the highest "you." I have only glimpsed my higher self, but credible people have become more themselves and can describe it. It is hard to comprehend how your choices are more preprogrammed than controlled from a source deeper within you that is more you connected to the power of being fully present and self-aware. One way to conceive of this is to think of times when, out of jealousy or anger or foolishness, you have done things that are not like your normal self, that you would never normally do when you are more centered, settled and yourself. There are various degrees of being you. That is just a lower you coming back to a moderately higher you.

Q *When I'm in that inner place, housed in silence and stillness, void of most everything else except my aliveness, how can I function if I can't think? I didn't quite get that.*

A You can be the master of your mind and body, even if you don't know how you're doing it! You'll have to experience it to believe it.

Q *I understand why someone would want to experience painful or uncomfortable things from a place of emptiness, but why would anyone want to experience pleasure, like great sensations and good times, from emptiness, with detachment?*

A Being neurally inshifted from pleasant sensations adds to the pleasantness. Sending energy into the higher parts of your brain is enjoyable. Detaching from pleasant senses-body states-mind-activity actually allows you to appreciate and enjoy the sensations and information all the more! It has to do with letting go—when you don't try to hold on to them or change them in any way, that allows you to more fully experience the sensations. If you aren't trying to intensify good feelings, like stretching out pleasurable times or holding on to happiness, they fill you up even more. Yogis try to make a similar point. They show that welcoming the pain (as just energy) of sleeping on a bed of nails or walking on hot coals is the same as neural inshifting to all of life's pain. This shows that meditation is useful for more than attaining some idea of ecstasy and nirvana from a quiet meditation room.

Q *How much effort is needed to learn to inshift? What is too much and what is not enough?*

A It can be tricky to know. It varies, depending on what level you are (beginner or experienced) and what your circumstances are (sleepy, troubled, driving or meditating). You may need more effort as you begin learning the steps to experience energy and draw it in. You may need some effort to actively learn to appreciate the sophistication and patterns of your mind and body.

Giving up direct control of your body, mind and life can actually take some effort. For example, habit and cravings can be tricky to let go of at first, like stopping yourself from scratching an itch. You need delicate effort to find silence and stillness, and, in fact, you need to stop trying at some point and just experience. It's like letting go of being anxious. You can try to relax, but after a point, you just have to stop trying and allow it.

There's a lot of effortless effort in inshifting, more so even in Steps 4 and 5, where you make somewhat of an effort in Step 3 and then allow Steps 4 and 5 to happen. It's like controlled falling backward. It's letting go. Remember, *at no time should you ever force any aspect of inshifting.* Force, as opposed to effort, is an indication of how off-track you are.

Q *How about the energy needed to Awaken?*

A Even less than Steps 4 and 5, there's no real effort that can make you Awaken. You need an intense amount of energy to stick with inshifting until you start to Awaken. It requires regularly practicing inshifting in spite of its frustrations, disappointments, discomforts, physical pain, emotional upheavals, self-doubt and so on. It's a matter of having enough faith and perseverance to hold on.

Q *What happens if, while trying to inshift, I forget what I'm doing and get caught up in some thoughts or a fantasy?*

A You will absolutely get caught up in fantasies and thoughts from time to time, often for most of the time you are intentionally inshifting. It's normal. Yet like the see-saw in Part 3, Figure 7 that describes brain regulation mechanisms, it swings up and down continually. The goal is to have it swing very frequently in the higher brain position. Perhaps you can hover there occasionally (with the swing pulled far down to the left). Inshifting is never a static skill, though, where your higher brain (you) can ever have complete domination over your lower brain. The real trick is to be able to come back to higher awareness quickly and often after it is taken over by automatic, reflexive and unconscious mechanisms.

Learning to inshift involves going through the steps over and over again as you get distracted in increasingly creative and different ways from your mind, body and outside events. If you can't enjoy that process to some extent, you will struggle the same as if you are not getting pleasure from each step. It will get overwhelmingly frustrating. It will exceed your ability to accept, detach and de-identify. It is one thing to witness and allow your lower brain to feel frustrated at the lack of perfection in learning the skill. It's another thing to set it up so that you are intentionally going to get frustrated.

Inshifting is a lifelong process for everyone, master and beginner. Back and forth, back and forth, over and over you bring yourself back to the inner place. Over and over, letting go of distractions. Over and over, deftly bringing back your attention, sharpening your ability to recognize the endless number of ways you get tricked into identifying with mind, body and life events.

Q *Can I really enjoy myself, relax, hang loose and be myself while I'm busy inshifting? It seems so artificial.*

A It takes time for inshifting to be natural. Learning any skill is awkward at first. You don't need to be totally relaxed to be inshifted.

Q *If my body feels relaxed for whatever reason, say I'm engaged in a fun conversation and having a great time, it all feels great. What use is there for making the extra effort of inshifting or for trying to use more of my brain?*

A Because your experience can deepen with the added joy of experiencing context in that moment at the same time. There are *no down sides* to using your higher brain to its fullest extent. To be fully present and aware of context, the extra measure of reflection, adds an immeasurable level of enjoyment and appreciation.

Q *Say I'm depressed after a breakup and raiding the refrigerator all night, even though I am fighting obesity. Can I still inshift and watch myself being neurotic or even depressed?*

A Yes. It's actually easier to realize what it is to find a state of inner peace and perspective when you are depressed than when your mind is happy! Very strange, I know. It's the same phenomenon as when you find inner silence in a noisy room. When you're sad and raiding the refrigerator, it is possible to have an even deeper appreciation for the significance of this moment in your life. It is like seeing the irony and poignancy of the emotionally painful times in a movie. Fully making a choice to allow the experience, feel the feelings and witness the events as they unfold brings a seemingly paradoxical inner satisfaction. It enriches your life to experience the full range of emotions and events. Awakening includes experiencing the fullness of a life.

Q *What role do balance and grounding play in my ability to inshift? How or where do I find them?*

A They're important. There are many things to balance, including just letting go and being empty. You find balance within you in *just the same way* you find your physical balance. It's natural. It's there. Being grounded is being settled in your body, which helps find balance and helps you shift your experience of body, mind and life into the background. Try this: as you sit in your chair, feel the balance it takes to keep from flopping over. Then, to fully feel that balance, feel the groundedness as your body resists the force of gravity in your buttocks, legs and feet. Those sensations center and anchor you.

Q *If I run into a distraction, like the annoying buzz of a fly, should I try to block it out? Is that what disengaging or de-identifying means?*

A One of the main strategies of inshifting is that you do *not* have to block out anything. Instead you shift everything into the background. So if you find you are distracted by a noise or a thought while trying to inshift, for instance, you disengage from either one by allowing yourself to experience it more fully, but from a place of silence and stillness. In other words, make sure all aspects of your senses, body and mind are in the background, in relation to the energized foreground experience of aliveness in each unique moment.

Q *How much help can I realistically expect to gain by learning to inshift well?*

A Quite a bit. Besides all the wellness benefits that you read about in Part 1, that most precious and sought-after stage of living is possible in your lifetime by learning to inshift.

Q *How critical is it to learn this skill? I'm not a patient person, and I don't have much time to spend.*

A Inshifting is critical. True, it is the skill that helps you fulfill your incredible potential, the skill that can bring you the peace, meaning and moments of ecstasy that you are capable of.

Yet, without learning to inshift enough, life usually and quickly fills with difficulties, from the nagging feeling that you are missing something to feel complete (regardless of how much money, love or material possessions you have) to outright misery, bitterness and even suicidal thoughts. Inshifting can be the one thing that helps you take advantage of other wellness and therapeutic strategies. What could be worse than living and dying without ever fully knowing what it means to experience an Awakening, to feel the ecstasy of liberation, to gain the understanding of an enlightenment? Especially if you were perfectly capable of it and it was right there in front of you.

Q *Can you give me some life examples of what it is like to be inshifted and why it would be helpful?*

A Here are three.

Imagine. You're driving home from work and your mind runs through the day. It relives a heated argument you had with a shop clerk. You begin fantasizing a more satisfying ending, telling him how he was wrong, when you didn't earlier. After a while, this becomes tiresome. But you keep repeating the same lines. It's hard to stop. Like a bad song that gets stuck in your head, it becomes annoying to keep coming back to the same story. Then you remember to inshift.

You allow the imaginary conversation to keep going, but you begin to feel the steering wheel, your hands, the rest of your body. You relax, you energize. The inner dialogue tamps down and becomes less intense. You feel less involved in it. You're in more control. The incident begins to fade as you become more detached from it and feel the sights and sounds of the road and become more aware of being here right now.

Sights, sounds and bodily feelings take on a new quality. They're lighter, brighter, more vivid and unreal. The freedom of indirect awareness takes stress off you. Frustration at your perseverative mind lessens and anger at the store clerk melts away just enough to feel it. Your mood is lightening up.

As you experience context for the insignificance of any one event, but the significance of this ROYAL Now, and immediacy nostalgia for the fact that in a few years' time you will miss being younger, the incident with the clerk feels like a distant memory. You drive in a better mood, enjoying the fluid movement of the car and its sensation.

Now imagine you're anticipating seeing relatives as you are packing for a trip to visit them. Then your twelve-year-old daughter wanders into the room. You stare in shock. She's decided to cut her own hair. Normally long and beautiful, it's now short and uneven, with ridiculously short bangs. You were so excited to travel, to see your relatives, to show off your beautiful children. You had everything well planned. You bought everyone new clothes.

Your mood drops. Instantly your trip seems ruined. The excitement drains out of your body. Stress and anger take its place. You ask your daughter, with thinly veiled sarcasm, if she's looked in a mirror. You wonder how she could be so thoughtless—why she didn't ask you before cutting her hair?—as your anger rises.

Then you inshift.

Accessing Point X immediately, you detach from your emotions and feel them as energy.

Suddenly, you more clearly see your daughter's hair and her anguished face. With distance you read her better. The situation, the moment, seems more absurd, different. You see for the first time how bad she feels. It is not about displeasing you, but about doing something childishly impulsive to herself. She suddenly looks pathetic. You see her as the little girl she is. Compassion wells up. You witness it. It signals you to reach out to her. You easily and spontaneously allow yourself to hold out your arms and she embraces you.

Sitting in front of the TV feeling agitated, you are thinking there's never anything good on anymore. Halfway through folding a large pile of laundry, the restless boredom is numbing. Then you inshift.

You feel the colors of the clothes in front of you. More exactly, you feel the intensity of the colors in your eyes. You feel the sound of the television in your ears, the images flashing past at lightning speed in your eyes, the sensations of the soft towels you are folding. Everything seems more vivid. It's instant relief from the boredom.

The moment seems like something out of a novel about a person in a life of drudgery, with you as the star, only you are witnessing yourself as part of the story. The story is satirical, funny, weird, interesting.

You continue folding towels while watching your hands in action. You're fascinated by the way your hands seem to know how to fold. Detached, you experience your hands seamlessly going from one towel to the next as the TV acts as a backdrop.

Then the feeling of the scene changes. From weird and interesting it gets deeper, more profound. This moment is a time in your life that you will miss. You look at your house, think about your life, and realize on a deeper level that this is your life, and you cherish and appreciate it.

Part 5

Wellness Inshifting

You feel good not because the world is right, but your world is right because you feel good.

— Vernon Howard —

Correct care and use of your brain is the key to a stimulating existence and ultimate contentment. Look after your brain.

— W. Richie Russell —

25

In Pursuit of Wellness

Are your desires purely selfish? Do your tastes run to a grand home, automobiles, fine clothes, an abundance of amusements and so forth? If so, look around you to people who have such things in superabundance. Are they any happier, do you think, than you are? Are they any better morally? Are they any stronger physically? Are they better liked by their friends than you are by your friends?

— B.C. Forbes —

Remember your wish list we discussed in Chapter 3, "Peak Well-being and a Great Life"? Now that you are acquainted with inshifting and what it means to Awaken, your wish list may be different. As you Awaken and begin to appreciate how extraordinary ordinary moments can be, your priorities will change and keep changing. Being rich and admired, and creating an "ideal" life with the right emotions, the perfect spouse, unerring friends, a model family, or an idyllic career will become less important for you as the deeper pleasure and fulfillment of an inshifted brain endures during the lows and highs of life. Even notions of ideal spiritual attainment become whimsical pursuits, life theater. The static ideal life cannot compare with a lifetime of "flawed" perfect moments flowing from one uniquely alive moment to the next, experienced from an inshifted brain.

So why concern ourselves with wellness and a wish list? First, because improving ourselves and pursuing ideals is what we do as humans—if in moderation. Second, wellness can be practiced and attained for the express purpose of creating an inshift.

To find items on your wish list, to find wellness and success while also growing and developing emotionally, psychologically and into higher realities, the full "neural-wellness" inshifting (NWI) approach requires a few things.

First, take responsibility for mastering your own brain. Take ownership of the ways it sees and reacts to things so you can learn to direct it. Seek goals, but detach from outcome, and outcomes will come. Learn to inshift with Awakening central to your goals for health, happiness and satisfaction.

Second, practice holistic wellness as a way to inshift. Use the strategies you'll learn here to make your *neural* inshifting easier to learn, or to make it happen automatically. For example, do weight lifting with detached awareness or eat with full intention. That will strengthen your skills. To make inshifting happen more naturally, for example, instead of changing your diet or exercising just to look better or even solely to lower your risk of a heart attack (which is a great secondary goal to be sure), eat and exercise so that you have the stamina, energy and release—the natural high—that causes an inshift. In that way, each area contributes to your Awakening (see Figure 13).

Third, follow key practices from *all* the wellness areas—physical, mental, social, cultural, moral and spiritual—*at close to the same time.* That can sound daunting, and maybe it is, but if you practice them all together, each area supports the others. Remember, good physical health improves mental health, and vice versa, around the wellness wheel. All the practices of each of the six universes act synergistically. This makes the wellness aspects of the NWI approach very powerful. Think of it: getting fit *and* finding new love *and* succeeding at work all at the same time is intensely energizing. It will cause a stronger inshift.

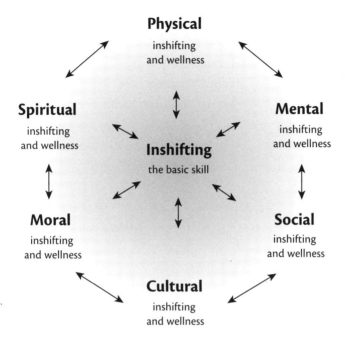

Figure 13. The wellness wheel: how wellness areas interact and are catalysts for inshifting

There are five principles that will help you in every wellness practice and with learning the skill of neural inshifting itself.

- Balance and moderation
- The specific balance of acceptance (being) with improvement (doing)
- Empathy for yourself and others
- Wisdom and common sense
- Following an inspired plan

The first principle, balance and moderation, is central. Buddhism has been called "the path of moderation." Moderation is not always walking the middle of the road—eating a meal with a compromise of the right proportions of healthy and unhealthy (yummy) food—although sometimes it is. Moderation can also mean knowing that *anything* we do can have seemingly opposite but potentially helpful aspects to it. In physical wellness, for instance, eating ice cream may drain you of energy, lower your immunity, cause weight gain and lactose intolerance, and so on, but it is a good thing to occasionally treat yourself and to help you appreciate life. Sometimes taking a calculated risk (bungee jumping, wearing something outrageous, staying up all night and partying responsibly) will bring you to a better balance of health.

This is not a wellness-to-Awakening cookbook. It offers dynamic guidelines, not a static recipe. Balance cannot be predicted ahead of time.

The second principle, the balance between acceptance and improvement, is so important to inshifting that it is called out as a separate kind of balance. You face two polarities in every practice, and really in every moment of your life. The first is the instinct to improve, change for the better and do the wellness practices that it takes to naturally inshift. The second is to first accept and appreciate things just exactly the way they are.

This comes up within your inshifting practice. Remember neural inshifting Step 3? We spoke about detached awareness, indirect experiencing. This causes you to let go of your senses, mind and body so that you accept and detach from them—even when your mind and body seek goals, desire more and need improvement.

This dual experience of indirectly experiencing your mind, its signals and goals while also experiencing energy puts you in the realm of total acceptance and allows your mind to do its thing. This is where the balance between acceptance and change first comes into play. Living in the world of information, with signals that help you avoid problems, meet needs and improve, and living in the inner world of energy, which must be accepted the way it is, is key to living life fully. And to Awakening. You appreciate the amazing reflection of this moment in time that is found in a messy room while you seek to clean it. You do both: you experience energy (acceptance) and information (change) at the same time.

The third principle, empathy and compassion, really does pertain to all wellness areas. That's because the capacity for empathy as a skill comes from accessing the higher brain. In the mental wellness arena, when you are inshifted enough to detach from your own ego, empathy happens: you approximate what it's like to experience something from the perspective of another being (humans and animals). Empathy causes compassion: understanding the world from another being's perspective, understanding who they are and what compels them to do what they do, gives you compassion for them, regardless of whether you agree with them. Compassion, love and caring are good for your health—that's a proven fact. And they make it easier to let go and feel alive!

Learning the skill of empathy, you can empathize with yourself! Empathizing with yourself is a form of mental inshifting. Using your higher brain to enter the reality of your lower brain seems like a psychedelic mind trip, but that is what you do when you inshift. Empathizing with yourself, having compassion for yourself, helps you accept, love and allow yourself to pay inner attention.

It's probably easier to see how the fourth principle of wisdom and common sense applies to every area of wellness. For instance you may read this book and think that adhering to a program of meditation, yoga, healthy eating, sleep hygiene, family meetings, household organization and civic responsibility will help you inshift. They will. But your expectations of what is required for wellness and Awakening might take you over. Wisdom and common sense give you perspective; they ground you to momentary reality. It is through wisdom and common sense that you can best discern balance and moderation. Wisdom and common sense can tell you when to empathize and when to assert yourself and how to find the balance between appreciating the unique-ness of each moment and wanting to change it. Wisdom and common sense are intuitive. They are cultivated by inshifting, and they in turn cause inshifting. It is with wisdom and common sense that you know what decisions to make about anything, re-ally. They direct you on your path to Awakening.

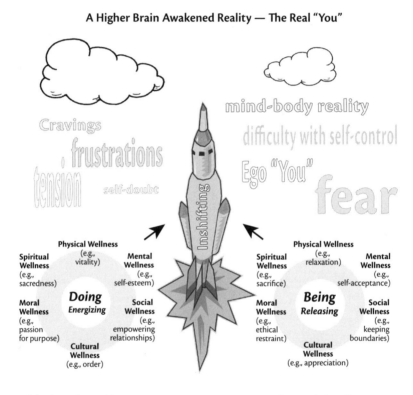

A Higher Brain Awakened Reality — The Real "You"

Striving for order and improvement   Acceptance and appreciation of what is

Figure 14. The balances between wellness areas

Figure 14 shows a metaphor for the balance needed between being and doing, acceptance and improvement, the fuel needed to inshift. It shows the fuel needed to launch you, "the rock-et," on your journey past anxiety and debilitation to health and

Awakening. As you pilot the spacecraft with inshifting, you fuel it with the balance between energizing/improvement aspects and releasing/accepting aspects of wellness. Perhaps this rocket isn't so much launched into the stratosphere of Awakening as it is that, when all the conditions are right, the cloud of ego dissipates and what is revealed is the perfection of what is.

We'll discuss the fifth principle of following an inspired plan in the next chapter.

26

The LifePlan for Awakening

*There is nothing so useless as doing efficiently that
which should not be done at all.*

— *Peter F. Drucker* —

*Apathy can be overcome by enthusiasm,
and enthusiasm can only be aroused by two things:
first, an ideal, which takes the imagination by storm,
and second, a definite intelligible plan for
carrying that ideal into practice.*

— *Arnold Toynbee* —

There are many wellness practices that you'll encounter in the remainder of this book. Keep in mind that there is no need to perfect or even practice every single one. However, to make coordinating them all easier, I developed a LifePlan for Awakening.

The LifePlan can make your neural-wellness inshifting (NWI) program more cohesive. It can help organize the various wellness strategies into a time management strategy to bring your NWI strategies to life. It also is a wellness strategy in and of itself that enhances inshifting. A sample LifePlan is shown in Figure 15. It is outlined as follows:

- Preamble
- Values and list of principles
- List of life roles or wellness areas (on a vertical axis)
- Visions for what you'd like to see in those areas (on the

horizontal axis) in the immediate next weeks, the intermediate months to a year or two, in the long term (years to come) and by the end of your life

- Specific steps that you must take to accomplish those visions in the immediate, short term, long term and end of life (on a different table's horizontal axis)

The preamble states facets of your identity (who you are) and your life purpose. It reviews and prioritizes your values and has you keep a running list of your life principles, many of which you can get right here from this book.

You then list your life's major roles and areas separated by wellness area, i.e., physical, mental, social, cultural, moral and spiritual. A physical role or area might be as an athlete or to prevent a specific disease, such as diabetes, or some representative aspects of your overall wellness you'll learn in this book, such as jogging, eating healthily, regular fasting and yoga. A mental role or area might be as a psychotherapy client or by coming to terms with a difficult childhood or personality self-discovery. Social roles such as spouse, child, parent, and profession are listed, as are areas such as assertiveness. Cultural areas might include financial management, home maintenance and disaster planning.

Next you *visualize* yourself or your goals in each of these roles and areas in the immediate, intermediate and long term, and then write action steps needed to accomplish them. That leads to a weekly, monthly and yearly time management plan that incorporates your action steps.

The acceptance of yourself that comes from naming your identity, the detachment that comes with seeing your ordinary self in your plan, the surge of energy and release from discovering a life passion, the ordered mind that comes from time management—all of this is an alternative wellness-inshifting track (as are all the wellness areas) to your neural inshifting process.

The LifePlan is something you can write out for yourself. The remaining chapters on wellness inshifting will help you fill it in.

The LifePlan for Chris Doe

Preamble

I am a 42-year-old Christian woman, mother of 3, daughter, wife and sister. My life purpose is to make the world a more visually beautiful place for generations to come through my art work. The 10 most important values to me are: love, truth, beauty, forgiveness, peace, empathy, passion, finding sacredness, family, friends.

My core principles are:

- A penny earned is a penny saved.
- Love your neighbor as yourself.
- Be a lamp unto yourself.
- Never punish your child in ways that are demeaning.

GOALS					
Life Areas or Roles	Immediate	1 year	5-10 years	10+ years	End of life
Physical *Exercise*					
Mental *Self-development* *Anxiety treatment*					
Social *Mother* *Wife* *Sister*					
Cultural *Finances* *Home org* *Disaster plans* *Travel*					
Moral *Art for* *neighborhood*					
Spiritual *Formal inshifting* *Retreats* *Church*					

ACTION STEPS					
Life Areas or Roles	Immediate	1 year	5-10 years	10+ years	End of life
Physical *Exercise*					
Mental *Self-development* *Anxiety treatment*					
Social *Mother* *Wife* *Sister*					
Cultural *Finances* *Home org* *Disaster plans* *Travel*					
Moral *Art for* *neighborhood*					
Spiritual *Formal inshifting* *Retreats* *Church*					

Figure 15. Sample LifePlan for Chris Doe

Each chapter first offers an overview of that wellness area and a brief discussion of the basic wellness needs you should consider in developing your own plan. Specific wellness strategies follow that discussion. With this arrangement you can refer to the discussions or to the specific strategies as you work on your own NWI plan over time.

27

Physical Inshifting:
Health and a Natural High

*If anything is certain, it is that the awakening process
ushers in a new era of health and vitality. It cannot be
otherwise, for your dynamic psychic forces now work
for your physical self, not against it.*

— *Vernon Howard* —

*A man must be healthy before he can be holy.
We bathe first, and then perfume.*

— *Anne S. Swetchine* —

Let's state the obvious again. Your brain is an organ, a biological tissue that needs water, nutrients, rest, blood and oxygen. Ionized salts keep and conduct an electrochemical charge across nerve cell membranes that sends electrochemical messages from one nerve cell to another. Without the exact balance of salts, you could feel really out of sorts or confused, or even have a seizure. Each nerve cell communicates with its neighbor with organic chemicals called neurotransmitters, which are made from nutrients and are affected by many different things, including Prozac, chocolate and sunshine. The more those neurotransmitters are off balance, the more you are as well. That includes what you feel, how you think and whether you hallucinate or cogitate on spiritual things. Even minor fluctuations in body chemistry (caused by, say, drugs, caffeine or alcohol), blood sugar, hormones, temperature, sedation, inflammation, or any number of things could cause you to be propelled into a natural high or dropped into a suicidal depression, all without lifting a finger.

Physical aspects of inshifting are the most important and fundamental wellness-based strategies for helping you inshift. You can learn to shunt attention and energy to your higher brain, but what if the energy isn't physically there?

Keep in mind that people have been known to have great Awakenings in the midst of extreme pain and terminal illness. The extreme feelings and thoughts surrounding those conditions may even have contributed to the detachment and inward focus. Yet preparing yourself gradually, readying yourself for crises and transitions, is what this book is about. And the anchor of inshifting your brain is in the body it's housed in.

General Physical Wellness Inshifting Strategies

Before we get into some specific strategies the first general idea to realize is that from the time we are born some of our cells are dividing and some are dying. We are always pushed and pulled by the ordered, building and energizing forces of well-being and the decaying, disordered and depleting forces of debilitation. The overarching strategy to finding health and vitality and keeping it is to stay on the energizing side.

What are some of the balances you'll need in the arena of physical inshifting? One is the balance between doing what is right for your body and giving yourself a treat. With food the question is whether you should "eat to live or live to eat." The answer is not an absolute.

Balance here is figuring which is right and when. Part of that is to know about where you are on the healing-debilitation scales: that's the concept of having a wellness "bank account." If you have taken good care of your body (you have "money" in the "bank") and there are no illness challenges ("debt") to spend those resources on, then go for it—have a rich meal and an ice cream sundae. Afterward, though, you have to build back your wellness bank account.

The other spectrum, perhaps more subtle, involves balancing different, competing optimal practices. For example, some of the choices you face are when to get rest or exercise, or when to fast or eat. The answers to the many balances have to do with having the wisdom and common sense to know your body and to know what is best for you in spite of what your body may be telling you.

A question you may have as far as physical aspects of inshifting are concerned is how to raise your energy level. You might assume that if raising natural energy causes some degree of inshifting there must be an easy way to get some energy, including drinking coffee and caffeinated sodas. The question is, would caffeine or even an amphetamine do the trick? As one of my patients asked me, half in jest, "Inshifting seems like a lot of work. Isn't there a pill that'll take care of it?"

The answer is that you have a good amount of energy stored up in the tension of your muscles and from other areas of your body, so tapping it is often enough. Yet, when you're sleep deprived or otherwise exhausted, artificial means of gaining energy are not usually the answer. They are often too intense, stimulating your whole brain and not just your higher brain. However, there are natural ways to increase energy besides neurally inshifting it from other parts of your brain and body. Most if not all the specific strategies presented below will provide you with natural energy.

Specific Physical Wellness Inshifting Strategies

Some people think vitamins and other supplements are the main answer to physical wellness and the question of feeling stimulated and well. However, "supplementation" means "to enhance or complement," not "to replace." It is irrational to think that you can eat unhealthily and load up on multivitamins and herbal products to "supplement" your way to vitality. There are specific supplements, though, that may aid inshifting.

Wellness Inshifting Strategy:
Supplements.

Use the right supplements that fit you unique physical and emotional needs for any one particular time in your life to help your brain function at its peak. This should begin with a broad-spectrum, high-potency daily multivitamin and mineral made from natural food. It should be strong enough that it contains, for example, 50-100 mg of the main B vitamins, which are critical to brain function. They also metabolize nutrients and clean the liver so that you feel calmer and more alert. Certain minerals are also key for brain functioning. Phosphatidylserine, the herb gingko biloba, and some of the amino acids used in the brain (such as L-tyrosine, DL-phenylalanine or L-tryptophan) can all be used to enhance neural inshifting if you receive clearance from a qualified medical professional.

Omega-3 fatty acids also lift mood gently and stabilize mild mood swings. They help nerve cell functioning. High EPA omegas are correlated with increased attention, and DHA omegas are linked to improved thinking. Take a concentrated form (most easily found in fish oils) as directed. Treat your brain right and it will respond in the way you need it to.

Other physical wellness strategies include eating and drinking the right nutrients and avoiding the wrong ones to provide strong and releasable energy. This comes with ingesting the substrates (like enzymes and fluids) your body needs, but also keeping your body clean by fasting and cleansing to detoxify and purify it. Here are some specific strategies.

 Wellness Inshifting Strategy:

Eat right!

Some foods, including dairy, meats, and salty, sweet and overprocessed foods, take so much energy to digest or excrete that they deplete the body of energy instead of boosting it. That's especially true if they are eaten in excess. Eating these foods can make you tired and even depressed. The right foods eaten in the right amounts increase natural energy. Haven't you ever noticed after eating a big, rich meal heavy in animal products that the couch and a TV are all you can manage? The right nutrition can help inshifting happen more easily and naturally.

Avoid more than small amounts of inorganic salts. These salts, like plain sodium chloride in chips, build up and raise your blood pressure, mess with your kidneys and precipitate (become undissolved and solid) in your body. Natural salts, though, are electrolytes involved with nerve conduction. So make sure you get enough salt in the natural hydrated form from celery and other foods.

Eat sugars like sucrose and high fructose corn syrup only in moderate amounts. Many simple sugars eaten in concentrated doses overstimulate the pancreas and disrupt the body's blood sugar level. This can cause restlessness and fatigue and can interfere with inshifting.

Avoid foods with additives, preservatives, artificial coloring and flavor enhancers. These foods build up in the body, are toxic and make you feel ill and depleted of energy over time. Eat as much organic produce as possible.

In short, eat fresh or lightly cooked edible plant-based foods. Eat a fresh vegan diet as much as possible! If you eat a wide variety of vegetables, fruits, grains, seeds and nuts, beans and legumes, you will find a natural balance of proteins, carbohydrates, fats, enzymes and nutrients. Plants also contain trapped energy fresh from the sun, which is a rich primary energy source. This diet also is high in fiber and easily assimilated through your gut. If you are in good health and have high wellness credit, eating 75% vegan should provide what you need. (A "high wellness credit" refers to how ahead of the game you are in your health, e.g., whether, because you exercise, eat well and take the right supplements, you can be considered at a low risk of illness and live in a natural high.)

If you take in food that is dense in rich and needed nutrients, besides being healthier and feeling a sense of well-being, inshifting will be unavoidable.

Wellness Inshifting Strategy:

Eat in moderation.

Even a 100% fresh and optimal vegan diet can be overeaten. Accumulated foodstuff that cannot be cleansed out of the body becomes toxic. Overeat, and the energy your body must use to digest and excrete that food will rob you of energy you'll need to inshift.

Wellness Inshifting Strategy:
Avoid strong stimulants.

Caffeine and other stimulants, even if used in micro-doses, provide unnatural stimulation that is so intense and so unsupported by the nutrients it needs to sustain it that we wind up depleted, de-energized and more tired. The higher brain can only accommodate energy that comes in natural forms or it crashes. If you want your brain to learn how to naturally raise its own energy to inshift over the long run, avoid stimulants.

Wellness Inshifting Strategy:
Drink enough water.

Most people are dehydrated to some degree. Yet, water is the medium for the chemical reactions that make us function. That is why water is so important: our bodies are 80-90% of our bodies are water. Drinking the right amount of water every day will help your body create the energy and release you need. Water is the major constituent of the cerebrospinal fluid that bathes the brain, another aspect of effective brain functions, such as clear thinking and mental calmness. Water also helps flush the body of accumulated toxins that can deplete your energy. It thins bodily secretions like saliva, lymph and inter-cell fluid, which is essential to the proper functioning of the brain and body. Drink at least eight glasses of water a day, but be careful: too much water can dilute your blood. Being hydrated makes inshifting that much easier.

Wellness Inshifting Strategy:

Fast regularly if medically approved.

Keep your body clean, with your arteries cleared of fats and toxins, your intestines free of buildup and sludge, your lungs free of dirty mucus; don't allow chemicals and toxins to build up in cells. Your organs will function better, and energy won't be blocked. Your immune system will improve and your lungs will oxygenate your body, which will help you feel naturally high.

Preventing a grimy, filthy, toxic body is the first rule. However, it's impossible to keep anything clean that is being used continuously, especially your body. Fasting is the most effective way to cleanse your body, although its health-promoting benefits remain relatively unrecognized in the United States.

Fasting must be sanctioned, if not constantly supervised, by qualified health care professionals. Fasting means not eating while keeping your body well hydrated with pure water, so that your body goes into a self-cleaning cycle to spend energy ridding itself of old, built-up, toxic, useless and obstructive substances. Cleansing fasts can take 24-48 hours. Healing fasts can go up to eight weeks. Both must be medically supervised.

Fasting is not starvation. Starvation rids your body of essential resources, such as muscle mass. Ridding yourself of harmful substances clears your body's passageways and allows for the assimilation of new nutrients and energy. The overall energy, calm and mental clarity that comes from a cleansing fast are amazing. In fact, in ancient times fasting was considered more of a spiritual exercise than a health-promoting one!

If cleared by your medical professional, undergo a water fast (or a raw juice fast, if a water fast is not allowed). The details, lengths and types of fasting are a subject beyond the scope of this book (find out more from the American Health Association). However, fasting is a science. Depending on your age and health, recommendations vary for how quickly you go into and out of a fast, how long you fast and what type of fast you should undertake. The average overweight American can live weeks or months without eating, as long as they are hydrated. The thought that you would be starving after a few weeks and unable to tolerate the hunger is exaggerated. Fasting teaches you about physical and psychological hunger. Psychological hunger occurs first. Then, perhaps because of ketosis, the breakdown of fats, this hunger is often followed by a physical high and a sense of psychological freedom from not being a slave to the next meal.

Remember, a lean body that isn't full of toxic and undigested sludge will fill you with the radiant energy you need to inshift effortlessly.

Much data has been collected documenting the benefits of aerobic exercise in health and wellness. Pumping blood, oxygen and nutrients through vital organs, including the brain, has been shown to do everything from relieving depression to preventing cancer and heart attacks. It's so well promoted in our culture that the point need not be belabored.

Wellness Inshifting Strategy:

Do aerobic exercise.

The more aerobic exercise, the better (within the limits of wisdom, common sense and your doctor's supervision). The recommendation is for 30 minutes of moderate to strenuous aerobic exercise, two to three times a week, where your pulse is kept within specific ranges for your age and condition (see any good book on cardiovascular exercise). This doesn't have to happen in a gym on expensive equipment, although a portable pulse meter is advised.

A body that has a strong heart and energized brain suffused with blood, oxygen and nutrients is a body that will inshift on its own.

Building physical strength, including posture, balance and muscle toning, is key to keeping you energized and vibrant while also keeping joints limber and muscles stretched. The ability of physical strength to make you feel calm and grounded should not be underestimated.

Wellness Inshifting Strategy:

Keep your muscles toned.

Do at least minimal core strength training (i.e., arms, back, abdomen, legs) so the muscles store calcium, a mineral for nerve conduction, and protein, a nutrient that creates neurotransmitters, which are chemicals that connect one nerve to another. Toned muscles will improve your posture, which is crucial to feeling vibrant and alive. They will also allow you to engage in long periods of formal inshifting practice whether you are moving or sitting still. Toned muscles give you strength and endurance. Try standing tall and grounded and see if you don't experience an energy shift.

Wellness Inshifting Strategy:
Practice daily stretching, relaxation and physical balance.

Incorporate mild stretching (without overstretching cold muscles) and relaxation exercises into your regular exercise routine, perhaps before and after exercising. Muscles hold on to tension. Reducing tension and freeing the energy flow of the body is an important ingredient to effective inshifting. Concentrated body balancing, such as standing on one leg, helps your higher brain find balance with its lower brain.

Wellness Inshifting Strategy:
Practice yoga.

In particular, consider practicing some yoga exercises before you do a formal, daily inshifting practice. Yoga, itself a form of meditation, allows the energy in your body to be released so it can be used by your higher brain for inshifting. Take a yoga class or watch an instructional video and do yoga exercises regularly, before you meditate and/or during the day when you feel the need for energy and centering. Include breathing, coordinated stretches, vertical postures and balance with interludes of relaxation. Conditioning yourself to inshift is the manifestation of wisdom.

 Wellness Inshifting Strategy:

Include tai chi or a movement meditation.

Do this at least before or after your daily inshifting practice. Try taking a tai chi class. If you decide to follow a sitting meditation form of inshifting (in addition to preceding it with yoga) follow it with a brief walking meditation or tai chi. Again, this is preparation for the challenges you will face in your NWI practice—it's priceless.

Our bodies and brains evolved in the wilderness over eons. In this flash of time that humans have had civilization, particularly within the micro-flash of modern years, we have made ourselves unhealthily distant from the natural settings in which we evolved. Although not as trendy as the health benefits you can find in a fitness center, a supplements store or natural-food grocery, getting out and about in nature, at least in city parks if not a remote wilderness, is essential. It is a restorative strategy for your brain, body and mind. When I hear the birds, feel the breezes and see the landscape, I automatically experience an inshift. Any effort I add to that becomes "icing on the cake."

Wellness Inshifting Strategy:

Regularly get out in nature or wilderness.

One of the most powerful yet subtle ways of inshifting is being in a natural setting, such as a beach, desert, forest, field or mountain, often and regularly. The effects can be dramatic. For example, the desert has been the impetus for many of the most significant spiritual realizations that have happened in recorded history, realizations that might not have happened in a busy urban environment.

The farther you are out in natural environments, the more inshifting happens, freeing you from the need to detach or try to be in the present. Even in the city such seemingly small gestures as opening your window to feel the air temperature makes a significant difference in whether you are trapped by the relative mind or empowered to experience the absolute world. We just seem to recognize the absolute world better in natural settings.

Getting a good night's sleep is critical to proper brain and mental functioning. However, unconsciousness is *not* the same thing as natural sleep. The average of eight hours of sleep has a structured architecture—it happens in well-defined stages throughout the night. That is why sleeping pills, which merely make you unconscious, are not good regular sleep agents.

Wellness Inshifting Strategy:
Practice regular sleep hygiene.

Arrange for eight hours of uninterrupted sleep. If you are having trouble sleeping, try these ideas: keep to the same sleep and wake schedule every day; avoid exercising 4-6 hours before bedtime; avoid stimulating beverages and foods like coffee and chocolate; create sleep rituals, such as bathing, before going to bed; and don't stay in bed if you are stressed about not sleeping.

If you're tired, you will struggle to inshift! Period. In fact, the more exhausted you are, the more you will experience the opposite of a neural inshift. Your higher brain will be dulled and your lower brain will be in high gear. You'll feel controlled by your mind and body states and distracted by your senses, and your body will be restless and agitated. We've all felt that. I'm just naming it in terms of inshifting.

Self-health is the practice of optimal healing when you are ill. Practicing self-health will prevent you from succumbing to debilitation, which can rob you of vitality. It is an algorithmic series of graduated responses to health-challenging conditions that give you the most control and help you get the best outcomes possible.

Illness and fatigue are in the same ballpark when it comes to inshifting. If you are chronically tired—even with the most subtle effects—it will be that much more challenging to inshift.

Wellness Inshifting Strategy:
Practice self-health.

Here is a stepwise process for dealing with illness.

- Practice NWI as a way to prevent illness and keep a high level of wellness. In addition, become a keen observer of subtle signs of illness, such as energy and sleep changes or unanticipated weight loss. Address early, mild symptoms (such as starting to feel run down, scratchy throat, mild headache) naturally by doing such things as easing up on stress, resting more, drinking more fluids, cutting back on unhealthy foods, getting fresh air, making sure that your environment is cleaned and sanitized, and so on.

- Address mild to moderate symptoms (such as a cold) by trying over-the-counter natural remedies (e.g., garlic, zinc and vitamin C for colds) and homeopathic remedies that can be found in most pharmacies and grocery stores. Over-the-counter conventional remedies, such as antihistamines and painkillers, should be used after the nutraceuticals have been started and are not enough.

- With more intense symptoms (a persistent cough, flu, nausea and vomiting) it is a good idea to find a naturopathic (i.e., N.D.) or allopathic (i.e., M.D. or D.O.) doctor who is concerned with your whole body and being. If you see both kinds of health care providers, inform them of each other, and learn when to consult each. Both working effectively together is called complementary medicine, especially if you see a specialist. It does require you to understand and become an active partner in your own health care.

Psychiatric medication plays a role in inshifting—occasionally a critical role. Some people may see this as an unusual statement for a book that is largely oriented toward natural approaches to higher states. Of course, there is a balance to this as there is to every other strategy. Yet, psychoactive medications can be indispensable for someone suffering from a brain-based illness that affects their mood, sleep and appetite, thinking and reality. Medication along with inshifting can be central to help you move out of the "something's wrong with your brain" level of reality (remember that from Part 2?) into higher levels of reality. So can psychotherapy, which is a special case of inshifting. The secret is balance.

 Wellness Inshifting Strategy:

Psychiatric medications.

Use psychiatric medication strategically when medically indicated so it is used to help your inshifting, but not at such high amounts or for so long that it impairs your ability to inshift. (There are exceptions to this rule.)

28

Mental Inshifting:
Control and Insight

The root of sanctity is sanity.

— Anne S. Swetchine —

Blessed are those who can laugh at themselves,
for they shall never cease to be amused.

— Anonymous —

We are what we think.
All that we are arises with our thoughts.
With our thoughts we make the world.
Speak or act with an impure mind
And trouble will follow you
As the wheel follows the ox that draws the cart.

We are what we think.
All that we are arises with our thoughts.
With our thoughts we make the world.
Speak or act from a pure mind
And joy will follow you
Like a shadow that never leaves you.

— Buddha, in the Dhammapada —

Imagine that a team of psychologists has been studying your life since your birth. (We'll say your parents gave them permission.) Since you are an adult, these psychologists are prepared to offer you a detailed account of their findings: a recap and explanation of the events and people who have affected you most, including the results of extensive testing of your intellect, personality, ability to relate to others and talents and challenges. You find it amazingly accurate.

How would that affect your inshifting?

What the psychologists have presented is the mental programming of your lower brain. The better you know your mind, the less controlled you are by it and the more you'll learn where the inner you lies.

Awareness of your personality, what makes you tick, how people have molded you, your deepest beliefs, your emotional triggers, your wants and aversions, and what you are likely to do or not do can help you detach from all of these things. Your mind can naturally fall into the background of your experience of life as the immediacy of being aware and alive each moment shifts to the foreground. Self-direction and mastery arise from this: the ability to direct the reactivity of your emotional buttons.

That is psychological or mental inshifting. It comes from mental wellness practices.

Now, let's revisit the mind-brain model we discussed in Chapter 15. That's where we saw the see-saw between the higher and lower brain areas. We saw the ways each area controls the acquisition and use of information in your brain, the memories and behavioral patterns and other kinds of schemata associations. The result is that each area of your brain can use itself to create your reality! Each determines how and what you experience, what you do and how you act. In essence, mental health and mental disorder depend on how much of each area of your brain is used.

Remember what the lower brain areas do: they are triggered by stimuli that cause you to react automatically. The higher areas use your abilities to reflect on your own awareness (reflective awareness) and self-direct (spontaneously conscious choosing and authentic expression) to determine reality: what and how you experience, and what you do and how you do it. We went through the tug-of-war between the robotic part of you and the inner master, the opposing areas that underlie whether you make a fool of yourself getting drunk at a wild celebration or that same wild celebration fills your soul with its sensations, connections and poignant meaning.

So what happens when they both play on you at the same time? What happens in the middle, when the see-saw is more level, when both automatic and executive functions are both working more or less at full steam? It is in those more frequented places that the issues of your psychology really arise.

Remember the schema ball that rolls back and forth on the see-saw? The area where it gets released (processed) depends on the various combinations of lower and higher brain control mechanisms in play, and on how powerful the ball is. At different parts of the see-saw there are four levels of experience and functioning (see Figure 16, which shows the see-saw between the automatic/unaware system of the lower brain and the reflectively aware/volitional system of the higher brain).

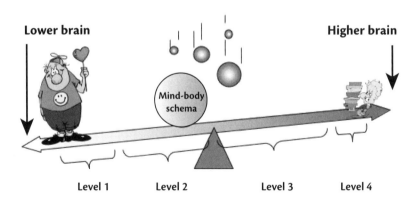

Figure 16. Levels within the spectrum of ego-based experience and behavior

Level 1, at the automatic end, describes how you experience and behave when you are completely to almost completely on autopilot, controlled by reflexes and programming. An extreme example is responding to sounds while in a coma, but more common examples are jumping after a loud noise, driving without being fully aware of what you are doing, unconscious slips of the tongue, behavior that is so impulsive you are barely aware of doing it, and so on.

Level 2 is where all the psychology of your mind and body's programming comes into play. Psychological problems arise when you get stuck at this level. It is where you are influenced by automatic programs, but instead of your awareness being gone or diminished, your awareness is passive. It's the level of illusions—what Albert Einstein called "the optical illusion of consciousness," where you live in a mind/body reality and your behavior is based mostly on habit, although you think you're directing it. Examples include lacking insight and being stuck in a particular role, being suggestible, superstitious, over-reactive, rigid, compulsive and obsessive.

In Level 3 you're still under the illusion of your mind and body, but your awareness is active, so you can tightly control your behavior. It is where your attention can be concentrated on one thing for long periods of time, where you are very deliberate in what you do and in how you think, where your thinking is measured and logical.

Level 4 has the most consciousness and self-direction (as opposed to tight self-control). In its extreme, where your reflective awareness is at its peak, you can "see" through the illusions of your mind and body. Your behavior is highly spontaneous and authentic and your thinking is highly intuitive as you Awaken and are liberated from the powerful effects of other people's and popular culture's influences, where you transcend your personality and the limited sense of "who" you think you are (your ego), where you perceive universal interconnectedness, and where you have piercing empathy for people, insight into the nature of the physical universe and ecstatic "peak experiences" (a term coined by Abraham Maslow) of aliveness. Less extreme examples are people who are wise and flexible, who don't personalize things and have an easy maturity, who have emotional intelligence, and who are highly authentic, intuitive and compassionate much of the time.

You can experience each level in an instant, depending on how powerful the stimulus that triggers your programming is, how powerful the programming is, and your level of awareness and self-control at that moment. As a style, you can also hover in each level in longer patterns of being and doing.

Most people hover a lot at Level 2, which is not a good thing. For young children it is good to have a firm belief in who you are and in your identity: it's part of the normal developmental process of the human mind. Yet as you reach adulthood, it is better to have a flexible sense of who you are so you can adjust to different situations and fit into more environments—so you aren't an annoying tourist who insists on having things the way they are back home.

This is where ego comes in: a lot of what mental inshifting is about is being aware of ego and letting it go. When your awareness is passive, it allows your mind free rein to create its main illusion, which is to relate everything inside and outside to itself (it's an "I" or "me" screening tool). The more passive your awareness (even though you seem on the outside to be fully alert) the more ego will dominate your personality and experiences. If there is no active higher brain way of being aware of things, you drown in an ego reality. That's the "traffic-is-all-about-me" type of angry egocentric reality. Note that I distinguish egocentric ways of perceiving things, where you misinterpret events, from egotism, or the view of an all-encompassing "I," where you take egocentrism to the extreme of believing you are more special than others and entitled to special treatment. Both come from an overactive, undirected lower brain.

Ego is also all about being insecure, self-conscious, anxious and depressed. So, again, a lot of mental inshifting has to do with learning to recognize your ego.

To prepare to do the exercises and strategies for each level, it is important to understand the principles in effect at each one. Your lower brain and the psychological conditions of your mind are different at each level. The main strategy is not just to find and return your brain to Level 4 functioning, but to learn how to control your lower brain at whatever level it may be functioning at any one time. Gradually you'll learn to return to being your true self, in Level 4, quickly and often.

Now, let's go into these levels in more depth. The strategies and exercises for each level are at the end of each section.

Level 1

Level 1 is one of no awareness, or greatly reduced or bypassed awareness. It happens when you're asleep or awake and sedated, confused by a toxic brain or intoxicated.

In Level 1, when you experience yourself running to the refrigerator every time you turn on the TV, you'll know that your mind and body are being controlled unconsciously by connections between the stimulus of the TV and hunger. In that way you can inshift from a place of understanding. The principle in effect is that when a stimulus, such as the sight of a TV, is repeatedly associated with another stimulus with a built-in response, such as the sight of food making you hungry, the first stimulus can cause the response without your awareness. That's why if you're used to eating while watching TV, you'll automatically get hungry when you turn it on. This is called classical conditioning and happens normally without any awareness, which is why it's a Level 1 principle. Watch how and when this happens in other circumstances, such as being unable to sleep in a bed that you associate with sex or TV. If you're used to snacking when you get home from work, you could pair the sight of your house with hunger. If you see how these associations can control your mind and body, you'll begin to inshift from your conditioned lower brain.

Practicing is an important strategy for Level 1 awareness that can prepare you to respond instantly in an emergency or major life event.

Predicting Level 1 conditions is an important tool for making inshifting easier. When you consciously replace one set of beliefs with another, you are inshifting!

If you often eat by the TV, you should know that sooner or later you will become hungry just turning the TV on. Many things automatically trigger a response. Trigger management is a form of inshifting. It means learning which otherwise neutral triggers in your environment unconsciously set off actions and thoughts. You use the knowledge of those triggers to prevent losing control and to mold your brain to your advantage to help you do more of what you want.

Wellness Inshifting Strategy:

Stay alert.

Get enough sleep, avoid intoxicants and harsh stimulants, and follow the recommendations in the physical inshifting chapter that keep your brain healthy and naturally stimulated.

Wellness Inshifting Strategy:
Subliminal programming.

Learn to anticipate and take advantage of opportunities when Level 1 conditions are going to be present (very low or waning awareness). That's when your mind's programming is triggered quickly in the absence or impairment of your awareness.

You can override awareness with relaxation tapes that have words embedded in the music that subliminally trigger relaxation. Hearing those words, without any awareness of them, automatically triggers a relaxation response. The same thing happens in movies, where brand name products are embedded in the background to cause you to pick those products in the store. Inshifting benefits from a lower brain that is controlled and organized even if it's not because of the immediate influence of the higher brain.

Of course, you can only do what your brain will ultimately allow you to do. So anticipating when you will be exposed to subliminal advertising (such as when watching movies) will help you be more vigilant and inshift to make the stimulus less subliminal. You can actually counter the effects of subliminal advertising by being aware of the phenomenon of having ideas implanted in your brain. Make a conscious effort to see the effect of billboards, TV commercials and ads on your mind. Don't allow advertisers to do an end run around your awareness. See how many branded products you can detect in movies or on TV shows, then note how your mind is affected by them. The awareness alone will help you control your impulses to act on these embedded temptations. The more inshifted you are and the stronger your skill, the less anyone else will be able to trigger schemata in you without your permission.

 Wellness Inshifting Strategy:
Practicing.

Practice or rehearse a few critical skills that you'll need in an emergency, such as performing an emergency earthquake drill or CPR, so that if you must respond automatically, your awareness will not be overridden. The ability to stay aware is the difference between spontaneous action and blind acts in important life events. It is like practicing a sport so that during a game you can execute your moves more spontaneously when there isn't time to consciously think through each step.

Ordering and controlling your lower brain, even when it is not being immediately influenced by your higher brain, will ease the process of inshifting.

 Wellness Inshifting Strategy:
Affirmations.

Program yourself with affirmations, with conscious repetition of sentences or phrases that build health, self-esteem or success. Affirmations are positive and constructive statements, self-instructions to your mind, that program it to do, think, believe and react in ways you consciously desire. To directly enhance your inshifting you might repeat to yourself, "I wake each day and discover uniqueness," "I don't need the approval of other people," "I am not my thoughts and feelings" or "What I am is a calm center in the midst of activities and sensations."

Create other affirmations that fit other areas of your life geared toward specific events and areas where you may need some assistance. Repeat them to yourself when you need them, or post them somewhere where you can read them on a daily basis. Again, programming your lower brain to conform to the control of your higher brain is not cheating—it's clever!

 Wellness Inshifting Strategy:

Trigger management.

Watch for times when your brain is automatically triggered (meaning you don't know why) to eat, get tired, feel anxious, get angry, think about sex and so on. Then figure out what could be triggering those things, and manage the triggers by changing the triggering stimulus (read a book instead of watching TV), uncoupling the programming (stop eating and watching TV at the same time), and being so aware of the programming and its triggers that you can be spontaneous and alter the outcome (when you feel hungry as you turn on the TV, control how much you eat or don't eat). Triggers can also keep you from doing things. For example, if you watch TV in bed, you may not be able to sleep. If you have insomnia, try not watching TV in bed.

This is another example of using the conscious intentionality of your higher brain to direct your lower brain. This is clearly a variation of inshifting.

Level 2

Level 2 is about illusions of the mind. Illusions are built by your lower brain. They happen when your mind and body are programmed to always seek rewards and avoid punishments. That means your mind is controlled by other people and by your environment. (Of course, the trick to inshifting here is to recognize that what is rewarding and what is punishing can change like the wind and be totally altered by your conscious choosing.)

Illusions of your mind get cemented in when your higher brain just goes along for the ride. That's how you get stuck in habits of experiencing, thinking and behaving. It's how you get fooled into believing things about yourself, others and the world that are not true!

In a Level 2 state of passive awareness *you think you are in charge, but you aren't!* Captive to your impulses and driven by outside factors, you have difficulty with eating, saving money, finishing projects, keeping organized, drinking alcohol or smoking, managing your anger or anxiety, any number of things. When your awareness is passive, *you may think you know who you are, but you don't!* You *are* whatever mind programmings are being triggered and reinforced.

Managing consequences is where you get to mess with the rewards and punishments in your life and indirectly learn to inshift. You can change what is rewarding and punishing to you and manipulate rewards and punishments to control your mind and body with your awareness. You can manipulate outcomes, exert intellectual control and directly inshift. However, you must first be aware that there is an issue: that your mind-body is struggling with the power that consequences have over it.

Remember, intelligent and conscious maneuvering of the senses, body states, mind activity, and actions (SBMA) of your lower brain requires that you be neurally inshifted. If you learn these strategies and apply them to yourself, you will inshift without necessarily being aware of it (until now, of course).

Wellness Inshifting Strategy:
Recognizing patterns of behavior.

Recognize your inner child and parent. Recognize the programming that has you default to being either a child or a parent. Find it when you get into trouble in your relationships in the same way without knowing why, as in repeatedly getting into the same arguments or choosing the wrong partner.

This has to do with childhood programming cemented in by continual rewards and punishments. If you get rewarded or punished enough for being a particular kind of child and imitating particular adults in your childhood, you will become them when triggered by situations that remind your brain of your childhood. Simple enough to fix? You know better than that!

This is how you can discover this programming. Again, this strategy is a form of inshifting and requires you *to* inshift.

So, say you were raised as a younger sibling and got blamed for doing things that your older sibling did. Whenever you are in a situation that even remotely reminds you of being blamed unfairly, a younger sibling schema can take over and cause you to experience reality at that moment (or longer!) as if you were a child again. If you are good at inshifting, you might catch this as it's happening. Otherwise you might catch it after an interaction with someone who reminds you of your brother or sister. If your inshifting, and hence your insight, is impaired, you may never realize it and become stuck in that role!

You can easily recognize this type of programming whenever you have extreme emotions around someone in particular, usually to the point that you feel out of control. For example, think of shaking in your boots with your boss, being enraged at your children or spouse, or cut off by another driver.

This strategy requires you to be at least a bit practiced at neural inshifting so that the recognition of this kind of psychological inshifting can really take hold and transform you.

 Wellness Inshifting Strategy:

Recognizing familiarity.

Recognize familiarity as rewarding. What is rewarding is often that which is familiar.

Familiarity may seem benign enough. It's why young children often choose macaroni and cheese and peanut butter and jelly over new tastes they usually end up liking once they learn to override familiarity (or they're persuaded to eat differently). Yet, familiarity is the reward that keeps you in the child or parent role from childhood. Familiarity will drive you to be with people who are like you and in situations that you have already experienced, keeping you from discovering new people and situations. The rewarding aspects of familiarity may be part of the root of prejudice and even conflicts between societies that fear what is unfamiliar.

Remember, seeing novelty is an inshifting skill.

 Wellness Inshifting Strategy:

Recognizing outer pleasure.

That which is motivating isn't always *good* for you. Outer pleasure (mind and body pleasure) is not the same thing as inner pleasure. Inner pleasure is deeper. It turns into bliss and ecstasy.

Think of having that last beer before you drive home, because being high feels so good. That's outer pleasure. Thank about taking that one last chocolate and piece of cheesecake from a buffet when you struggle with weight loss, because it fills your mouth with delight. Think about letting yourself have risky sex, because it feels so wonderful. Think about basking in the sun for hours, risking melanoma, because it feels so warm and cozy. These are examples of outer pleasure.

Then, on the other hand, recognize that what you would normally consider punishing is not always *bad* for you. Think about inshifting and resisting an interesting thought while dealing with a bit of frustration as you learn to pay attention inside you.

When you come to experience outer pleasure as different from the pleasure of deep relaxation and stimulation that comes from an inshifted state, your life will be on track for an Awakened level of well-being. When you can experience that what is aversive can be used to stimulate you, your life will be freed for an Awakened liberation.

Wellness Inshifting Strategy:
Manipulating outcomes (or contingency management).

This strategy is to find what rewards your lower brain and use it to make your lower brain do things.

Say you know you have a problem pushing your plate away at the end of a meal or putting too much on it in the first place. If you are consciously motivated to lose weight and to look good, buy yourself an expensive outfit that is the size you *want* to fit into! It is a desirable outcome that can't be altered. If that outfit is a strong enough motivation for you, it will dampen your desire to eat. Or, resolve to give yourself a reward, like a massage, for every five pounds you lose. Of course, the trick is to find a reward that is powerful enough to make you want to resist the impulse to eat. You must take the time to be thoughtfully creative with this approach.

You can also manipulate outcomes in your mind, which requires neural inshifting beforehand. Say you are unexpectedly involved in a sexual situation that is genuinely not in your best interests, but you feel yourself succumbing to the moment, to the sensual pleasure. You are ambivalent: your rational mind says "no," but your body says "yes." Consciously implant opposing images in your mind. Imagine yourself looking in a mirror and seeing genital or facial herpes, or being pregnant, or being observed waking up next to this person in the morning. It's a nasty trick to pull on yourself, but it does illustrate that controlling outcomes can consciously strengthen the awareness and self-control of inshifting.

Wellness Inshifting Strategy:

Observe your inner voice.

Again, this requires some ability to inshift beforehand, but it also strengthens your inshifting ability in return.

Listen for your inner narrator. You know, the one who argues with you at the buffet table when you are coming up to the chocolate cake, saying, "I shouldn't. Sit down *now!*" And then, right before you snatch up the chocolate cake, "Oh well, life is short. I'll diet *next* week." That voice is not you. It doesn't come from your higher brain. It seems like it's the real you speaking, but it isn't. It's the programming of your lower brain that has a voice. But, if you don't recognize that, you'll be at the mercy of your drives and rationalizations and conditioning.

Learn to recognize the narrator as not being you. Then consciously use it to discern different viewpoints and intellectualize an answer. Whether you go through a decision tree or just know what makes sense, with that level of energy your answer is backed up by self-control.

Wellness Inshifting Strategy:

Channel the energy of consequences.

Let's go back to the buffet table. There is that mouthwatering chocolate cake, and you feel ambivalent about taking it. Inshift to the point that you can channel the energy of your hunger into greater awareness.

That immediately puts you in more control. This gives you the distance, the detachment you need to engage your reflective awareness and to be able to self-direct. Then you can more easily engage your intuitive and logical faculties, weigh the pros and cons, or just do what you know is right.

Level 3

Active awareness is the skill involved at Level 3. It is using your thoughts to control what you pay attention to. You could rightly ask why it's even necessary to call this out as a skill, since it is hard to conceive of paying attention to something if you don't think about it in the first place.

It is true. Attention and thinking do go hand in hand. In Level 2 what your mind caused you to think about and feel emotions about and what your body caused you to crave or recoil from is what grabbed your attention and hence your awareness. That's passive awareness. In Level 3 active awareness involves your higher brain controlling your thoughts so that it directs your attention and awareness. Where awareness goes, so goes your reality.

You may rightly ask again how deliberately controlling your thoughts to focus your attention and act deliberately has anything to do with the neural inshifting skill you learned in Part 4. (Remember, the skill asked you to let go of using your thoughts to lock in attention, so that you can find a higher source of control and an inner place of awareness.) Perhaps you can think of the strategies in Level 3, as well as the strategies in Level 2, as neural inshifting Steps -1 and 0. They are ways to further prepare you for the strategies in Level 4 that are more closely aligned with the five inshifting steps you learned in Part 4.

Active awareness requires you to control your thoughts so that you think logically and rationally, think yourself through situations, understand yourself in words, rationalize emotionally difficult situations, describe events to yourself and rationalize your behavior. Think of Spock: "Yes, Captain, that is the logical conclusion." When you make active use of your inner narrator, you're using a Level 3 skill set.

The inshifting strategies of Level 3 involve making rational sense of situations so you can feel and act in ways that you choose. The strategies here were derived from the field of cognitive psychology and the works of such leaders as Albert Ellis, Aaron Beck and David Burns.

 Wellness Inshifting Strategy:

The causality cure.

Learn that events and other people do not "make" us feel, think or act. Shift into a higher brain reality and you will clearly see that you are in more control than you realize and that you actually make *yourself* feel, think and act by the way you choose to interpret events. You *cause* yourself to feel, believe, think and act.

Mental inshifting has you look at your emotional life as if you were a scientist, able to shape your emotional reactions when you want by seeing things objectively, by being an expert on the workings of your mind and body.

How many of us are aware of the hundreds of times in each day that we blame our feelings and thoughts on outside events? Really understanding this idea, in all the ways it affects you, can mean the difference between a life of unhappiness and intense suffering or Awakening.

 Wellness Inshifting Strategy:
Choose to believe.

In Level 3 you can make a rational choice to believe things that make you happy and at peace and help you inshift. This is different from using affirmations. You don't have to believe your affirmations. That happens unconsciously. Here you *convince yourself* with a better thought or belief. You can persuade yourself based on the merits of the different alternatives. It gives you more indirect control over your mind-body because you are directing it how to think. Observing your rational mind free itself from its own ensnared beliefs and expectations can be an important tool in self-liberation.

Find a situation in your life that is causing you distress. See how your interpretation of events may be seen different ways. This is hard. You can get so stubbornly fixed in your opinion that it is very difficult to see things differently, especially if you feel hurt and angry. Test your ideas. Ask yourself if this makes sense or ask other people if they would interpret the event the same way. Choose the more rational explanation and let your mind come to peace and to a more inshifted state.

Wellness Inshifting Strategy:

Digging to core beliefs.

Go deeper with your mental inshifting by exploring the ground floor of your mind's programming. Fundamental beliefs about the world, the universe, yourself and others that were formed early in your past are called core beliefs. Because these basic assumptions influence who you are at your core, and were usually created before you knew words, they can be invisible to you and taken for granted, although they are always in front of you (like your aliveness). There are many beliefs that you are probably easily aware of, though most usually extend out of one of these core beliefs. If, through direct neural inshifting, one of these beliefs comes to the surface, it can be very difficult to detach and witness it objectively. That's why this exercise can make your inshifting easier and more productive.

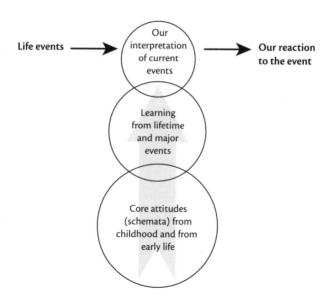

An example of a core belief is if, as a child, you were given everything you wanted right away. You might come away with the core belief that the universe is a place of never-ending plenty, but maybe also that you are entitled to whatever you want, whenever you want it. That can affect how you see things now.

Other examples are your belief in gravity, that the world should be fair, whether this is a welcoming world, whether the world can meet anyone's needs, whether you are lovable, whether you matter, whether people can be trusted, and so on. The idea of core beliefs is from psychologist Albert Ellis's ideas on what he calls evaluative beliefs.

When you catch yourself feeling strong emotions, look for these signs of core beliefs:

- They are absolute ideas: black or white, all or nothing, good or bad, "have to be," "will definitely," and so on. When you catch yourself thinking that things have to, should, or must be one way or another (rather than would be better one way or another), you've probably captured a core belief.

- Core beliefs also come in the form of dramatically exaggerated hyperbole: "The world will come to an end if that happens," "It is, was or will be the worst possible thing imaginable," "I couldn't stand it," "I would die," "I'd rather die," and so on.

- When you find yourself drawn back to a child-like feeling, for instance, as if you are a child being punished, you are tapping into core beliefs and attitudes.

- When you grossly over-react to a life event, to the point that even you can easily recognize that you went overboard, you have probably come close to a deeply held core belief.

Wellness Inshifting Strategy:

Counter core beliefs.

Recognize core beliefs and you will inshift. Counter those beliefs when they don't serve you and you will inshift. Do this by using a rational response to irrational beliefs formed in your childhood. Counter these beliefs using whatever experience of neural inshifting you have. So if something doesn't go your way and you catch a core belief that the world should be fair, a counter from an inshifted experience might be, "The world is as it is. Acceptance of that can help me feel relief, happiness and inner peace."

Wellness Inshifting Strategy:

Act as if.

When you "act as if" you are inshifted or mature or evolved, you are *pretending*. Pretending is a way of fooling your lower brain and body into doing and believing what you want it to do and believe. Acting brave even fools your body into secreting hormones that can support your courage.

Try acting as if you are fully alive and present. Try sitting up straight, spine erect, body relaxed, energy channeled to your alertness, and act as if you are energized from within. Act as if you are at inner peace.

"Acting as if" is similar to the Alcoholics Anonymous notion of "Fake it until you make it." Motivational and spirituality author Vernon Howard coaches you to "act as if" when he asks you, "How would you feel if you had no fear? Feel like that. How would you behave toward other people if you realized their powerlessness to hurt you? Behave like that. How would you react to so-called misfortune if you saw its inability to bother you? React like that. How would you think toward yourself if you knew you were really all right? Think like that." (Howard, 1969)

Level 4

We've talked about reflective awareness and the choice, spontaneity and intuition it allows. Reflective awareness happens when part of your attention is pointed directly inside your head, inside the place you use to imagine things. There the clearest reality comes to light: only "now" exists, and only reflective awareness can experience it. That experience of "now" comes from sensing aliveness. It is a sense beyond words, and in such control that senses, body and mind just seem to know what to do. You are clearly master, but no thoughts are needed.

In this place of open clarity the psychological principle of "means-end reversal" is best used. What this is has to do with your higher brain being in such control that it can switch a means to an end and the same end to a means. For example, a rat will run in a wheel just to get food, and it will eat when it isn't hungry to get access to the wheel when it needs exercise. That "means-end reversal" is forced on the rat; you, however, can do it voluntarily when you learn to let go of immediate control and detach your mind from its automatic quest of the goal and its automatic use of the means to get it. Rewards and punishments are not absolute, but rather a matter of perspective. (Think of someone with the sexual proclivity for what others would consider painful.)

We have the capability to take that to a higher, conscious level. We can experience things as rewards or punishments at will. Religious people willingly tortured for their faith have been remarkable examples of "means-end reversal."

 ### Wellness Inshifting Strategy:

Means-end reversal.

Learn the ability of means-end reversal. A good example of means-end reversal is that a hungry rat will run a wheel to get food, and the same rat will eat more than it wants to get access to running a wheel for exercise. In other words, depending on the circumstances, rewards and even punishments are relative. Moreover, a human can actually choose to experience any stimulus as rewarding or punishing. Pain is punishing to one person but enjoyable to someone who is into sadomasochistic sexual activity.

You can learn to choose inshifting as rewarding. It can seem tiresome and even burdensome when you are low on energy or attached to worrying or some ingrained emotion. Choose the extra bit of effort to allow relaxation, inner stimulation, detachment, clarity and the sense of being alive as rewarding. Learn to find pleasure in things most people would find neutral or boring, such as the flow of energy in each moment.

Choose to have the process of life be more rewarding than the outcomes. Choose to experience the uncomfortable feelings that may arise when you are inshifting as rewarding, as a measure of success—

even if it means feeling boredom, anxiety and restlessness, and having to let go of interesting or pleasurable thoughts.

Now to Level 4 aspects of ego.

Ego makes up some of our most core beliefs. It is all pervasive. Part of the normal development of a young mind, ego is brain software that helps it deal with infinite amounts of information, organizing around a theme and a way of perceiving, which is an "I" or "me"—your identity. Ego puts things, people, situations, feelings and thoughts into neat unitary perspectives. You have to deal with only a few categories: what is *for* you, *about* you, or *you, not for* you, *not about* you, or *not* you. Everything is screened this way. It makes life less complicated for a growing person. When you reach adulthood, the ego should begin to *dissemble a bit at a time,* replaced by a nuanced worldview and mature, Awakened ways of being. Unfortunately, that rarely happens to a high de-gree. Of course, people mature emotionally, but most are still trapped in their ego. Unless transcended by a major life-altering event, a deliberate inshifting practice has to be approached from many different angles.

Your mind's ego feels like you. It is an exceptional set of cases of a means-end reversal because its beliefs are so fundamental to your unhappiness. Transcendence of ego is foundational to an Awakening; in some circles, transcendence (of ego) and Awaken-ing are considered the same thing. It is the lion's share of what mental inshifting is about at Level 4.

You can recognize your ego in its *competitiveness.* Part of what it means to be ruled by your mind and your bodily impulses is that an ego develops that continually needs to compete and compare itself with other people. There are two aspects to this comparison: so you can know how you rate and how good you are, and so you know if you are normal, mentally well and fit in. There are healthy and unhealthy sides to these two aspects of your comparing ego.

It is important to recognize how your ego makes *comparisons*. Have you ever tried to not appear crazy or weird? This comes from the ego's programming to compare itself. Of course, like the other aspects of ego this is a built-in program, part of being human, although to transcend it is to see it as programming and supervise it.

Your mind is also programmed to acquire things to survive and so can be driven by *relentless desire*. The problem here is that even when you don't need to worry about surviving, your ego is programmed to assume that if a little bit is good, then more is better.

Wellness Inshifting Strategy:

Recognize the different manifestations of your ego.

Recognizing your ego is another way to inshift. It takes a state of detachment, quiet inner clarity and grounding in now. See the many faces of your ego, such as defensiveness, insecurity and relentless desire, as unconscious ways you learned to find comfort, safety, meaning and identity. Then learn to reverse that: from a place of inshifted inner comfort, safety and meaning in being alive, watch and supervise your ego and it will serve as a source of important information. (Transcending ego doesn't mean getting rid of it; sometimes it's a useful tool. It means to experience it as not you.) That's a Level 4 means-end reversal.

Wellness Inshifting Strategy:
Recognizing ego in superiority and inferiority.

Treated disrespectfully, hurt or deprived of love and nurturing, your ego hardens to protect its soft inner core. Ego congeals into a self-image that you use to keep from feeling vulnerable and hurt again. It scans the environment. It screens for things that might hurt you.

There are two halves to inferior-superior ego. One half is made of beliefs of being special and powerful, like the fantasies of being rich, famous or powerful you pretended to believe as a child. The other half is its polar opposite—feeling "less than," disreputable, unlovable, stupid or incompetent.

Both halves are two sides of the same coin, reactions to the same kind of childhoods. The superior part keeps you from being hurt, and the inferior part keeps you from being disappointed. Recognize this aspect of your ego if you often get into conflicts, sabotage yourself or are fearful of success.

The paradox is that you actually *are* special and totally unique. You cannot be replicated. No twin, no clone, no robot can ever *be* you. The experience of being you cannot be copied or simulated. Once the world loses you, the mold is broken. As modern physics points out, *the universe is different and permanently altered just because of your awareness of it.*

If you think you are exempt from superiority-inferiority ego, you may want to think about it or look inside more carefully.

Wellness Inshifting Strategy:

Recognize ego in a victim-perpetrator role.

As strange as it may seem, you can make yourself feel unique and special by *believing yourself to be persecuted and victimized by life.* For instance, do you feel life should be fair and that it is unfair to you? That victim mentality is your ego telling you how unlucky you are. In a similar vein, you might victimize someone else out of the ego-thought that life has treated you unfairly, so why not pass it along.

There is no crime to admitting these things. In fact, there is the beginning of what religion calls salvation, and what I call Awakening from ego.

 Wellness Inshifting Strategy:

Recognize ego in your competitiveness.

It is useful to rate yourself. To know how you compare is to be able to measure yourself in healthy ways, such as with medical indices or academic test results. Where it gets unhealthy is when you compare yourself with other people to find out if you are worthy, when you find yourself always "needing" to be ahead, like when you're driving on the freeway and you keep up with speeding traffic. Doesn't it feel demoralizing to be the one who gets passed or even to be a passenger in a car that is being passed?

We can never be good enough to measure up to the criteria set up by our ego. Of course, many people are okay with themselves for the most part, but most people have some vulnerability, some area where they feel "not as good as." Some feature of their body, some perceived deficiency in their intellect, physical challenge, a lack of some talent … something. Even being a second or youngest child can rev up your ego and make you compete for attention.

 Wellness Inshifting Strategy:

Recognize ego in comparing.

Learn to recognize when you are automatically comparing yourself with other people. Find it in your need to know if you are normal. See it when you need validation to feel comfortable with your own feeling and with your own beliefs—when you need others to tell you that your thoughts and feelings make sense. You can do that for yourself, although being validated by having someone empathize with you helps you let go of your comparing ego. It is also useful when you struggle with psychosis—when you are told that you believe things no one else believes and/or it seems crazy even to you.

See comparing ego when you are obsessed with fitting in, when your hair or outfit must be "just right." Remember that even being anti-establishment, say by acting and dressing different to be different, is being controlled by comparing ego. A conforming ego keeps you trying to follow society's standards or reject them, instead of transcending your ego and learning who you really are.

Wellness Inshifting Strategy:

Recognize ego in your relentless desire.

Do you look at elegant houses, beautiful landscapes, handsome cars or attractive people and wish they were yours? There's nothing inherently wrong with that. Sometimes it's fun to look at realty listings when you visit an area you love. The problem is that ego gets obsessed with desire if it is not counterbalanced with executive control and higher awareness.

There are reasons why your mind gets set on a relentless ownership track. Acquiring things is a temporary high, a substitute for spiritual joy. When you own material things, travel or go to the theater, your ego tells itself, "I matter." It compares itself with others and thinks, "I'm better" or "I'm worse."

Wellness Inshifting Strategy:

Recognize ego in negativity.

Negativity sounds like this: "My luck is always bad. Life is hard. It isn't supposed to be like this. The people in my life don't fulfill me. People are basically no good, out for themselves, you have to roll over them or they'll roll over you." Know anyone like that? See it in yourself?

When you've inshifted and are at peace with yourself, things don't look bleak and negative. The ups and downs of life are absorbing, interesting. Bleakness can look beautiful, at least from an artist's viewpoint. When you find yourself wallowing in negativity, bitterness or cynicism, see it as a symptom of a mind that has been hurt and disappointed. Use it to inshift. Let it be. Watch the wallowing and use it to find inner peace.

 Wellness Inshifting Strategy:

Recognize ego in your prejudices, aversions and judgments.

Let's assume you're a relatively decent person, not overtly prejudiced, basically welcoming of people from different backgrounds. Sound like you? Then imagine you're tired, had a bad day at work or some bad luck, and you see a group of people who look foreign. Now imagine that they are accidentally obstructing traffic when you're in a hurry. Can you feel your aversion? You tell yourself you shouldn't feel that way. You do anyway. That's your judgmental ego. See how you feel at ease and comfortable with familiar things and people. Recognize how people who are different by way of age, race, gender, social status, sexual orientation, religion or mental illness cause you to feel detached, negative or uncomfortable.

How do you weaken ego's grip? Think about what your first reaction is if someone argues with you. If you are like most people, you react by getting defensive. That is your ego. We're protecting it (as if there were something to protect). This triggers a number of ego reactions, from a feeling of superiority to competitiveness and grouchiness.

Wellness Inshifting Strategy:
Welcome opposing viewpoints.

Look for the opportunity to let your ego get inflamed by allowing yourself to hear arguments that you don't accept or by hearing opposing political or religious ideas. Validate that the other person's perspective can make sense and empathize with it. See how much it can change your opinion without letting any opinion become you. See how changeable your opinionated beliefs are and how they are not you—they can be observed and not clung to.

Be changed by criticism. If someone attacks you verbally, who gets hurt? You could say that the other person gets hurt and you would be right. Their anger removes them from the peace and joy of an inshifted state. You could say that you get hurt by the attack, but the question is, "Who are you?" The silence and stillness of your higher brain, which is your deepest experience of being you, cannot be hurt by name calling, accusations, critiques, lies or truths. You cannot be pegged as one thing or another—a bad person or a liar or a thief—if you are not identified with those things.

If an accusation stings because it is true, if a criticism hurts because it is accurate, then accept the truth of it. That's your higher brain controlling its mind. The sting or hurt will point your ego out to you. Ego is so hard to transcend that it takes many tries and many opportunities to be aware of it and disengage from it. This may seem odd, scary and awkward, but it has been a spiritual technique for centuries. The Christian adage of "turning the other cheek" is similar; if you or your ego is under attack, welcome the attack as an opportunity to loosen ego-pride and gain self-awareness.

 Wellness Inshifting Strategy:
Invite criticism and negative feedback.

Ask for critiques. Hear them as fully as you can. Feel the bristle—it's okay. Feel the shame, embarrassment, humiliation or anger. That's the effect of your ego being recognized and exposed. Breathe into that place of inner silence where there is no stress, and experience the emotional storm as it passes. It may be one of the most difficult things on Earth to do. This task is so painful that I believe it is the main reason why people fight.

If you pretend that you are *not* feeling what you are feeling, it may unravel the benefit of this life practice. If it hurts, it is okay for it to show. The humiliation from your emotional reaction is another layer of ego that has nothing to do with who you are inside. Your job is to train and take control of your lower brain by exposing it to the reality of what it is: fallible. Just never forget that your existence is an unimaginable gift, no matter how many mistakes or embarrassments you endure.

In Level 4, learning the skills of intuitive problem-solving can help you balance and, through practice, achieve an inshifted state. Again, it's a way to learn to inshift from a different angle.

Wellness Inshifting Strategy:

Intuitive problem solving.

Learn and practice the skills of intuitive problem-solving. These skills usually involve similar issues because most of the decisions we make in life impact our inshifting and so could be considered moral. Regardless, the same technique is used. Essentially, it is to posit each alternative in our mind. With detached awareness in an inshifted state of energy and reflective awareness you flip though the alternatives; when one matches the inshifted state, or a new synergistic, creative solution arises that furthers your inshifted state, that's the right one.

We've spoken about many Level 4 mental wellness-based practices that can help you inshift. Here's another scenario. Its purpose is to remind you that *direct neural inshifting* itself can be used to help you deal with the emotional troubles you encounter in life.

You're depressed. It's a long, dark winter. Work has been frustrating. You're not functioning well and you often have headaches. Several coworkers really don't seem to like you, and they talk about you when they think you're not aware. You're also worried because they're close with the boss, who has been critical of you in the past.

There have also been some major unplanned expenses and your credit cards are almost maxed out. Things at home with your family are tense because you've been moody and testy with everyone. No one seems to like you very much these days. You don't even like yourself. Today you come home exhausted and sad, feeling like crying.

Then you remember you can inshift.

In the first moment, it's really hard to contemplate inshifting. You imagine needing to be energized and vibrant, relaxed and in touch in the face of this draining sadness that feels like a weight drowning you. You just want to curl up in bed, but you decide to try anyway.

You start trying to feel Point X, but you can't feel it right away. Immediately you feel even more frustrated and sad, so you try again, feeling your entire body. That's happening a bit. You feel it. You add in the sound you hear, and a touch of relaxation happens. Even that little bit is a relief.

Sitting with the sensations of your body, with more release, the relaxation is more noticeable. Having the emotional weight lifted actually gives you a bit more energy to bring into your head. With that energy, you realize how much tension you've been holding.

You gently feel Point Y. It's a bit more centering and grounding. "Okay, this feels good," you think. Then another wave of sadness washes over you as you remember your day and your petty coworkers. A lump of sadness fills your throat. Almost ready to give up neural inshifting, you start over, feeling your body. Again you feel a release and are energized inside your head. This is not the exhilaration you normally experience when you've intentionally inshifted before. This calm energy feels like anger.

That heavy and depleting sadness is being transformed into clear and focused anger, as opposed to what could have been uncontrollable anger. It feels good. You think about your coworkers in a new light. You realize how much they have brought you down. Calmly energized, you realize how much your financial anxiety has brought you down. Only you're not afraid at this moment. It's as if you are waking up from a bad dream. "I've let these things bring me down," you think.

You do more inshifting. Detached and indirectly aware while imagining your life circumstances, there's more of the same: anger-

generated and tension-releasing insight. You resolve to be assertive with your coworkers and to face your financial anxieties with action. You're going to apologize to your family for being so difficult, using the self-deprecating humor that you can now feel.

29

Social Inshifting: Empowering Connections

*For many of us today ... intimate relationship has
become the new wilderness that brings us face to face
with our gods and demons ... When we approach it
in this way, intimacy becomes a path—an unfolding
process of personal and spiritual development.*

— John Welwood —

*Spiritual maturity is an acceptance
of life in relationship.*

— Jack Kornfield —

Whether they are sitting cross-legged in a snow-laden monastery in the Himalayas, bent in fervent prayer in a sweltering Indian ashram, or dunked in the holy water of an ancient cathedral, people have relied on other people to help them Awaken. People have passed down various methods, both religious and secular, through the generations. As you take your brain on its journey into Awakening, you will need to rely on other people for guidance and instruction, inspiration, encouragement, support, motivation, company and modeling. Communities committed to higher development have provided the foundation for inshifting (regardless of what they called it) for generations.

People can also assist you in one other critical way: they help you feel compassion and empathy, also forms of inshifting. Seeing the world from another person's perspective, understanding their beliefs and feelings, putting yourself in the place of someone who disagrees with you, even feeling the suffering of an animal all give you an invaluable way to inshift. For the time you are empathizing, you transcend your ego-drenched world.

People can also be your greatest challenge to your ability to stay inshifted. They can insult you, tailgate you on the freeway, reject you and break your heart. Can you contemplate experiencing those things while staying inshifted? People can take your will to even *want to inshift* at those times! These are the kinds of challenges people pose to your inshifting practice every day, often every hour.

Humans evolved from being a pack or troop animal, like dogs and apes, to a tribal species. Your brain evolved to function best in groups of families joined together by blood or other deep ties. For that reason you are likely happiest, better able to cope with stress and more apt to develop to the highest level of psychospiritual maturity in an empowering community of people.

As human civilization has changed, for example, as the Industrial Revolution took hold and people became more mobile, we started moving away from home, family and communities. Individuals and families became isolated from their roots. Roles began to deteriorate. And people often turned to meditation to escape the loneliness of modern life.

This fundamental change in social structure has had a significant effect on your brain. Without the intimacy, the logistical support and the identity of belonging to a tribe, your mind lacks order. Once again, a disordered mind can be a good challenge to your inshifting.

People can be isolated even if they know many people, because it is intimacy and connectedness that rids you of isolation. If you find that you are isolated, whether as an individual, couple or nuclear family, you will constantly struggle with inborn instincts to belong to a tribe. If you are in too large a group, or you don't protect yourself from being crowded, stifled or overcontrolled, you and your brain will be challenged. The balance here is to use your inshifting to enjoy solitude while also being able to feel powerfully connected and able to assert yourself when necessary.

In the 21st century, being in a tribe or forming and maintaining an intentional community or tribe is not easy. It requires the skills of interdependence.

Interdependence is a dynamic, fluid state. It balances the best aspects of dependence and independence with its own unique features. Achieving a balanced and vigorous interdependence requires empathetic listening and communication skills, sacrifice and boundary setting. To accomplish this it helps for all parties to be able to intentionally inshift at least to some degree.

Say you're riding in a Greyhound bus on a long journey. The guy sitting ahead of you seems like a rough biker type. He cracks open a window and sneaks out a cigarette, and smoke billows your way. You don't like to breathe cigarette smoke. You look at the front of the bus and the sign: "No smoking."

How would you handle the situation? Your reaction would depend on how fearful you were of him, how annoyed you were by the smoke, how offended you were by a rule being broken, or how diplomatic you could be. In essence, it would depend on your assertiveness.

For example, in the above case it might help to first imagine how difficult it is for a chronic smoker to go without a cigarette for a long period of time. Detach from your anxiety about confronting anyone, let alone the stereotype of someone with an edge. Expose your beliefs about the worst-case scenario, such as being stabbed and killed on the bus, to the clarifying reality of this moment, and reason and intuition will better guide you. Allow yourself to act compassionately but assertively to spontaneously know what to do. The answer is as individualized as the moment.

You might let the cigarette smoking go. With empathy, you might not care as much. Or you might say to the man, "Excuse me, I realize this is a long trip and it's tough to not smoke, but it's getting into my sinuses." Without ego, recognizing there could be a compromise, you might add, "Is there anything you can do about it, like open the window more?" You might just wait to hear his solution.

Just as inshifting itself and all the inshifting strategies are ways of taking care of yourself, being assertive is just as important. Being assertive requires inshifting whether you realize it or not, and assertiveness is another way to practice inshifting. The alternatives of being passive and living in irrational fear or being aggressive and over-personalizing everything are the opposite of being inshifted.

We all feel torn by choices that affect other people. Some are clearer, such as putting off the family vacation when the kids need expensive dental work. Some are not so clear, like when your spouse doesn't like skiing and you love it, so you need to negotiate vacations to ski resorts or tropical beaches.

Sacrifice for the sake of a family or relationship is perhaps the opposite of boundary setting. Today, any coupled relationship (e.g., roommates, partners, marital, work, friendships) is often based on meeting each other's needs. Yet for a relationship to succeed in the long term, at different times, one person or the other must make a sacrifice to keep the relationship going. Sometimes one person has to make all the sacrifices.

From a deeply inshifted viewpoint, where each moment alive is miraculous, the love you feel from sacrificing is releasing. It enlivens you even more. There may even be great joy in enduring pain for someone or some cause you love. It is a paradoxical notion, but one well worth understanding: not getting what you want or even need can bring peace and joy, if there is love, compassion and self-awareness in the sacrifice and giving.

It greatly helps to have support and encouragement when you're new to inshifting, rethinking your life, reprogramming your mind and engaging in different inshifting-centered wellness practices. The help and understanding, if not a shared sense of purpose, with your loved ones, friends and family can be important to getting anywhere with yourself.

More than anything else in our environment, people are a supremely powerful force. Our brains are programmed to seek and respond to people. We are a tribal species. We thrive in community with other people. The cooperation of a tribe can help make our time in the world easier, with less stress and more enjoyment. The motivation people can provide can be invaluable to our efforts to Awaken.

Wellness Inshifting Strategy:
Empathy.

Learn to empathize. Let's play a "what if" game. What if you were given the magical ability to leave your own body and enter someone else's? Privy to their thoughts, memories and feelings, and the way they experience the universe, you would be able to witness what it was like to have their problems, worries, aspirations, needs and desires, to see how other people treat them, and how they treat and feel about themselves.

How would you feel about that person after you came back into your own body and life? Would you be as judgmental of their faults and indiscretions? My guess is that you would have a newfound respect and regard for them. You would probably not take their issues, the ones that affect you, so personally. You might even feel a deeper love for them.

Learn to empathize to the point that you experience a significant inshift, where you are taken outside your ego and "I" views of the world. It's an ability that can be continually cultivated with practice. That skill gives you some of the sage-like wisdom attributed to ancient spiritual masters.

 Wellness Inshifting Strategy:

Assertiveness.

Learn to be assertive all the time. How do you learn inshifting by asserting yourself, and vice versa? First de-identify with and depersonalize situations that offend you. By not experiencing anything as exclusively personal, you have inshifted. Empathize with the person whose behavior is offensive. And seek a compromise. There just might be a solution that didn't occur to you and that works well for both of you.

 Wellness Inshifting Strategy:

Self-sacrifice.

Inshift to gain greater understanding of how self-sacrifice can be enlivening and even blissful. Practice giving. Self-sacrifice often. Give money that you might use for some luxury to charities and see if that feels immediately difficult but then invigorating. Sacrifice your own desires for the sake of other people's welfare, especially those you love, as much as feels reasonable intuitively and logically. See how giving and self-sacrifice make inshifting easier.

Wellness Inshifting Strategy:
Network.

Take the time to create, gather and nurture people in your life into an empowering network or even a like-oriented community, one that shares your desire for growth and development and isn't threatened by it. An empowering network could include the following:

- A couple: Two people, romantically connected, committed to making each other's welfare a top priority and sharing expenses, goals and daily responsibilities.

- A family: Two or more people living together, with daily contact and each other's welfare a mutual priority. They share expenses, have a common identity and common goals, and share daily responsibilities and a commitment to being together for life, if at all possible.

- A tribe or clan: Two or more families and connected individuals who get together at least weekly and share a desire for each other's mutual welfare. They share a common identity and/or regular rituals and tasks of living (e.g., religion, holiday and other celebrations, child care, logistical support, knowledge, advice and counseling, businesses, and civic or political involvement). There is a commitment to long-term involvement.

- Extended family: Biological relations or life-long friends who do not live with your family. There is a shared sense of history and/or biological and other identities. There is irregular contact at least once a year.

- Immediate community: A moderate-size group, e.g., a church, club or support group, where most, if not all, of its members know each other. Mutual concern is a priority, and there is a sharing in some regular rituals and tasks of living, with at least monthly contact and a commitment to longer-term involvement.

- Close community: A large group of people, e.g., a neighborhood, village, small town or local ethnic community, with frequent if irregular contact, where many people know each other and are committed to mutual concerns.

- Distant community: The largest group of people, e.g., state, nation or world, where there is some degree of priority for mutual concerns, such as defense or national pride.

To evolve with any speed and regularity you should examine which of these social structures you need, which ones you have, and, if you have them, if they are empowering. One way to define "empowering" is if the adult members are on a path of self-discovery and growth, if they understand what inshifting and Awakening are and encourage you or each other to pursue them.

If you aren't in the social structures you need, then you ought to work to form them or join one. The same holds for being in social structures that are irredeemably destructive to you and cannot be fixed. Form new ones from scratch or join different ones.

In forming or altering social structures it's essential to be clear about roles people have (e.g., leader, co-leader, member) and about supporting them in these roles. The roles within social structures are now more flexible than ever, yet that makes the definition of roles and functions more important! To clarify and empower roles, allow natural leaders to emerge; respect and acknowledge leaders, without allowing domination; assign roles to every member of every group, such as treasurer and secretary; hold formal meetings regularly; start and end meetings with sacred rituals and processing members' feelings; agree on the process for making particular decisions; and carve out time for social gatherings.

30

Cultural Inshifting:
Success and Acceptance

*What comfort, what strength, what economy there is
in order—material order, intellectual order, moral
order. To know where one is going and what one
wishes—this is order; to keep one's word and one's
engagements—again order; to have everything under
one's hand, to be able to dispose of all one's forces—
still order; to discipline one's habits, one's efforts, one's
wishes; to organize one's life, to distribute one's time ...
all this belongs to and is included in the word order.
Order means light and peace, inward liberty and free
command over oneself; order is power.*

— *Henri Frederic Amiel* —

*The true aim of mankind is the avoidance of pain and the
attainment of Bliss, yet owing to a fatal error man, though
trying to avoid pain, pursues a deluding something named
pleasure, mistaking it for Bliss. That the attainment of Bliss
and not pleasure is the universal and highest necessity is
indirectly proved by the fact that man is never satisfied with
one object of pleasure. He always flies from one to another.
From money to dress, from dress to property, thence to conjugal
pleasure—there is a restless continuity. And so he is constantly
falling into pain, even though he wishes to avoid it by the
adoption of what he deems proper means. Yet an unknown
and unsatisfied craving seems ever to remain in his heart.*

— *Paramahansa Yogananda* —

Walk through a Zen center and you'll be struck by one thing in particular. It's clean, and the gardens are more than well tended; there is subtle care given to the garden's design and balances. If you've ever seen a Zen rock garden, it has a clean, orderly and balanced openness, a freshness that reflects the mind of a brain that has achieved a degree of inshifting.

At the center, great care is given to cooking and eating. There is as full awareness as possible during food preparation, making sure there is self-control and even spontaneity in the movements of cooking and in leaving little if any waste. The financial ledgers are kept organized. The rooms are cleaned. All this is done by someone who is using these tasks as a form of meditation, to inshift. Rather than multitasking, being lost thinking of other things, they are self-aware.

Many religions and large movements have rules and guidelines meant to help you inshift, from how to interact with others, to how to settle disputes, eat, dress, contribute money and so on. Used in the right spirit, they can cause a neural inshift and ultimately contribute to an Awakening.

Cultural inshifting casts a wide net. Again, one of the reasons for attending to these areas from the perspective of inshifting is to learn *how* to accomplish them. How you go about them can help you inshift. Also, the result of managing these areas can reduce stress and help you feel ordered, which promotes inshifting. These areas include the management of stress, finances, recreation, fashion and cultural preferences, civic involvement, care of home and its equipment, personal and family time, and disasters.

Understand that there is nothing about owning a nice home, traveling, buying jewelry and attractive clothes and furniture, getting haircuts or watching TV that prevents or furthers inshifting. The question is how you go about getting these things, whether you approach your finances in a way that furthers inshifting and whether you allow them to become substitutes for the inner happiness of being inshifted. To help you neural inshift, you don't need to be a beggar, dress in plain clothes, not wear makeup or jewelry, or give all your worldly goods to charity. It does mean that with the order and acceptance of cultural inshifting you will feel an inner bliss that is more pleasurable than the *outcome* of material success, including approval from others. It's great to have a nice house and look good. But it isn't as important as the feeling of being in control and alive!

Material success and Awakening are not contradictory if there is balance. The humbleness, gratitude, compassion, life context, maturity, wisdom and resonance with purpose that come with transformative inshifting make it likely that you would use your material success for the betterment of humanity.

Ordinary aspects of living, however, would be impossible for someone well on the trail to Awakening who has an excessive amount of material possessions without sharing them, recognizing how unreal they are, or experiencing the greater amazement in the subtle.

Again, it's great to have fun and be successful as a way to learn to inshift. Inshifting itself and your higher self will provide balance so these things do not become more important than the experience of the inner you. Awakening to the miracle of your existence in each unique moment allows you to experience acquiring and appreciating material comforts in a new way, a way that makes life just that much more profound.

Now, before we delve into each area of cultural inshifting, let's talk about the balance between order and acceptance that you must be aware of to better use each area to learn to inshift.

In cultural inshifting order must come with acceptance. Imagine walking into your home one day, knowing a family member has stayed home with a bad case of the flu. There are clothes strewn all over their room, blankets and pillows on the couch, and empty containers and dirty plates on the floor. How do you go about creating a space that helps you inshift?

Before immediately cleaning it up because it is disgusting

and you want the space to feel energized and ordered, approach this task with the intention of inshifting. You might first feel compassion for the person with the flu, so that you clean from a place of love. You might experience this sickness and the mess as less an inconvenience than as a precious moment. You might see it as representing a singular moment (a ROYAL moment), part of the ups and downs in your all-too-short life that you'll miss one day. Appreciation helps with acceptance.

Acceptance by itself, without trying to be appreciative, is just experiencing your home as it is with detached objectivity. Don't just look at "the mess"—sense the visual and olfactory experience of that moment. Like looking at weird art that becomes interesting or beautiful in its own way, appreciation can follow acceptance. It leads to a ROYAL moment. Accept things the way they are before you seek to change them.

Intentionally developing cultural wellness skills—ordering your life with awareness and perspective, and accepting and appreciating things the way they are—is not just about finding ways to learn to inshift better. These skills are also your best shot at finding cultural and material wellness that is most fulfilling and meaningful. As Amiel says, there is power in ordering your life in the right way, without perfectionism and with acceptance.

In life we still have to deal with stress; the goal is to find ways to inshift and better cope with it. Stress related to modern living is insidious though—it's often subtle, affecting your brain, building up to the point that you can't stand it anymore. Let's explore the background of these brain stressors, starting with what our brains have evolved to deal with.

The first humans hunted and foraged for food and probably spent most of their free time with their families, sitting on a grassy plain in Africa, feeling the warm winds, contemplating the pattern of bark on trees, listening for predators and feeling the climate changes. Our nervous systems evolved to sense all the subtle variations in nature.

Time was different for them than it is for us. They were close to the cycles of the Earth and did not obsess about the future. They lived like our primate ancestors, in the social, tribal arrangement our brains evolved to function in. For our nervous system an emergency is equal to the fight-or-flight response; for our ancestors it meant an immediate danger, such as being attacked by a predator or being in the midst of a tribal war.

Now think about the stress that triggers your brain's fight-or-flight response. Unless you live in a monastery, the stress of modern living is constant. Examples are worrying about how you're going to pay bills, how your children are growing up, your coworker's rudeness, or even if there are seats on the vacation flight you want.

A human brain is basically the same brain as that of any primate—any gorilla or chimpanzee. So imagine how a chimpanzee would fare with the number of decisions *you* make in a day. If you drive, think about what is involved in an hour of driving: you must keep the car on the road at different speeds and in bright sunshine or stormy weather, adjust to other cars, and watch for pedestrians, children, animals and roadblocks while reading traffic signs and billboards, listening to the radio, changing stations, putting in tapes or CDs and talking on the phone.

Then think of all the complexities of modern living: filing a tax return, managing investments, keeping a budget, making decisions about how to spend your time, maintaining your home and vehicles, managing technological equipment and appliances, shopping for groceries, supplies and clothing, managing your family's health needs, and planning vacations and parties.

There is also the added stress of having your lower brain programmed for you by corporate marketing practices. A modern free-market economic system is a great system, but your ability to neurally inshift can be challenged when you are persuaded to buy or tricked into buying things you don't need. In commercials and other media you are exposed to overt and covert messages that try to make you believe you are inadequate unless you live up to some ideal; their solution is for you to buy products that promise that ideal.

The outcome is bad for your self-esteem and pocketbook; it weakens your higher brain by programming your lower brain. This obviously can make inshifting much more difficult. A major strategy in cultural inshifting is learning to be aware of the influence corporate marketing has on you and how it programs your lower brain's mind.

Then there is the stress of over-relying on technology because of this influence. Although technology has helped humankind enormously, marketing has exerted considerable power to have us believe that we *need* these tools. Do you really *need* computers, phones, PDAs, hair dryers or electric razors? You don't need them to survive, to be happy, healthy or fulfilled. There is bliss inside you. There is a heaven within. You can experience an Awakening.

You may want these things. There have certainly been life-saving technological advancements, but there is also a balance between the convenience and assistance we can get from such tools and the necessity of getting back to basics and simplicity. Simpler, more natural lifestyles might not require the gargantuan number of antacids, antidepressants and high blood pressure medicines sold.

Many of these things make accomplishing things easier. They *can* make your life temporarily less stressful and more fun, but wanting them so you will be happy can make you miserable and disappointed. They can make your life less fulfilling if you aren't careful. You can use inshifting to see technology as icing on the cake of life, not the cake itself.

Then there is the influence of the media all by itself. Movies and art are often more than things made for aesthetic appreciation: they often deliver a message to change who you are and what you think, and often with good intentions. Yet the full power of the media on our lives should not be underestimated.

Technology also has an effect on our brains. Sodas, chips and hot dogs are processed foods artificially enhanced to taste and look better so your body and mind crave them. Soft drinks and cigarettes are drugs that will make you dependent on them. Cars get you places faster at the expense of exercise. Calculators help you do math at the expense of cognitive sharpness. Computers take you away from the experience of natural environments.

So be careful. Remember that marketing agencies spend billions on psychologists, advertising experts and marketing campaigns dedicated to influencing your attitudes and beliefs. Stress can be invisible because you get used to living with high levels of it.

Wellness Inshifting Strategy:
Stress.

Know that stress is not what happens to you or what you put yourself through as much as how you react to it! How you react to anything, especially stressors, is the essence of neural inshifting. Learning this brain skill turns life into a series of nows. Stress is replaced by the pleasurable experience of energy flowing from one event to another. The relaxation and energy of that state overrides your fight-or-flight nervous system.

Let's consider recreation. Recreation is not a luxury. Some amusement and fun apart from your regular activities can work wonders for your health, your mental well-being and your spiritual growth. Playing, laughing and challenging yourself in enjoyable ways are energizing and releasing. A weekend of laughter and time away from routines and even from an all-consuming NWI program can bring you perspective and the lightheartedness that neural inshifting requires. This helps you maintain your basic mental health and launches you to higher psychospiritual states. However, recreation can take planning.

 Wellness Inshifting Strategy:
Recreation.

Learn to appreciate the importance of recreation to inshifting and to your health and well-being. Learn to plan for it and build it into your life.

Psychospiritual attainment can be found in even the most unlikely places, including fashion and popular culture. Minor changes in fashion can make you feel inadequate unless you continually revamp your wardrobe. Of course, there is nothing about updating your wardrobe that affects inshifting one way or another; in fact, being aware of the times you live in and being flexible can be allies of inshifting. However, you should be aware of why you buy new clothes, with the context, perspective and inner peace and strength to not *need* to do it. How can you inshift into a higher reality unless you are aware of the power that advertising and popular culture wield over your mind and your life?

The advantage for fashion designers and their advertisers is that everyone instinctively wants to fit in or stand out from the crowd. There is nothing wrong with enjoying fashion or wanting to look and feel good. However, letting others tell you what looks good and what doesn't risks allowing other people to define you.

It is inevitable that we, as a social species, are going to communicate with each other by how we dress and groom. In this sense, fashion is both a personal and cultural statement, a communication about who we are. Even avoiding fashion is still a statement. Are you a conformist, a rebellious, artistic, bright or casual person? Are you attuned to the culture around you?

It is normal to have your image of yourself, your sense of self, arrested at an earlier age in your life. Most people identify themselves with who and what they were in their late teens to early twenties, and your fashion choices may reflect that age. If you keep your awareness fresh and keen, you'll notice if you have a tendency to still dress and express preferences as if you were living in a former era.

The same thing that holds for fashion holds for all your preferences. Cultural preferences, such as your taste in music, the arts, what you think of as ugly or beautiful, and your formality of speech, are a reflection of what your mind has become.

Wellness Inshifting Strategy:
Fashion.

Watch to see if, with fashion, you are motivated by fear of rejection for not looking good enough, by shame for not fitting in, or by an inner joy and playfulness to look good (i.e., you don't need but enjoy fashion). Just noticing those things is a form of inshifting.

Wellness Inshifting Strategy:

Your self-image.

Look in the mirror. Compare the image in your mind with the image before you. Is there a mismatch? Are you okay with what you see? The older you get, the more incongruous the image becomes. If you do not fit the cultural ideal of beauty, you'll feel that incongruence as well. Inshift to cause that schema to change. Experience the image of your face and body from a detached and fascinated place instead of from your programmed lower brain. Do that and you have enhanced your inshifting skills immeasurably.

Wellness Inshifting Strategy:

Flexibility.

If you find that you are trapped in habits of experiencing and reacting to fashion and preferences, try exploring new tastes. It could be a powerful mechanism to inshift. Flexibility, the ability to change and adapt, is an essential feature of your higher brain. Remember, people get into ruts because familiarity is comfortable. Most of us enjoy the same music, visual art, theater and speech patterns because they are familiar. Inshifting opens you up to enjoy new experiences.

Wellness Inshifting Strategy:
Persona.

Create a persona for yourself as consciously as possible. Influence your lower brain by how you dress
and carry yourself. For example, if you are depressed,
get dressed up. Recognize that clothing and groom-
ing are aspects of your mind and body states.

Inshift to decide what to wear or what not to
wear, or whether and how to groom. Inshift to experience your cultural environment (e.g., what people are
wearing, how things are changing), your bodily needs
(e.g., how cold or warm you are, whether you have
any aches or are fatigued), and your mind (e.g., your
ego is to know how bright, outgoing, introspective or
laid-back you are, whether your identity is based on
your role, rank or ideology). Inshift to see the world
as it is, with as fresh and new an experience as possible. Detach, de-identify and disengage from the pull
to follow or rebel.

What about your civic life? Social activism and civic involvement are the traditional ways that people have used to Awaken a
sense of compassion, passion and purpose in their lives. Involvement in government and your neighborhood is energizing. Sure,
it takes time to vote when you have many other things to do. Yet
if you don't have enough time to vote once a year, look at your
priorities. See if they are out of balance.

Wellness Inshifting Strategy:
Civic involvement.

Use civic involvement and social action to uplift and energize yourself and to allow your mind to evolve to a higher level. Experience the energy from speaking up about an issue. Act on civic responsibility. Connect to your surroundings and the people around you. Participate in your neighborhood. Give back to the world using your unique resources.

Home maintenance is another critical component of social inshifting. Remember how consciously the Zen temple is cleaned and maintained? You should be just as conscious in taking care of everyday basics, of how you manage your home and your time. Ordering your home and time feeds back to your mind and orders it. Gaining awareness of how much it affects you, whether it lifts you up or brings you down, is a powerful way to use inshifting to find balance.

For practical and safety reasons it's critical to maintain your house, auto and home equipment. House fires are started by lint-clogged dryers. Roofs, furnaces and exterior walls can take tens of thousands of dollars to replace unless hundreds of dollars are put into maintaining them. Worn tires can blow out.

Of course, maintaining and understanding all the maintenance details can be time-consuming and not seem as important as spending time with family or exercising or relaxing. That's the balance needed with all wellness routes to inshifting. Balance requires prioritizing between wellness tasks. That's how your Life-Plan helps.

I believe the expression "cleanliness is next to godliness" means that being in a clean, ordered environment reflects the crisp openness of your inner self. Doing a formal inshifting practice in a clean space lends it an extra feeling of sacredness. Practically, cleanliness is good for your body and brain's health, considering how many allergens there are in our homes. The act of cleaning is also an inshifting exercise: aware sweeping, humble scrubbing and grateful polishing are tangible aspects of inshifting. Besides, you have to clean anyway, so why not practice inshifting at the same time?

 Wellness Inshifting Strategy:
Home care.

Maintain your home and the equipment in it so you can order your mind, feel in control and further your cultural wellness.

 Wellness Inshifting Strategy:
Maintenance.

Maintain all your house, auto and home equipment (e.g., electronics, appliances, furnace, roof, tires, brakes, lubrication) and keep good records. Be aware of your auto, house and home equipment with gratitude, so that you care for them and make them a priority.

Wellness Inshifting Strategy:
Cleanliness.

Keep your living space as clean as possible and the positive effects on your inshifting will be noticeable. With disordered surroundings you'll experience a greater challenge to your inshifting.

 Wellness Inshifting Strategy:
Scheduling needs.

Take care of your family's and your basic needs by being organized and planning ahead.

We often have a contradictory relationship with money, yet it, too, belongs in our inshifting model. The value of money—when you don't need it to survive—is mostly a projection of your mind. It takes the form of your ego when you use it for power and to get respect and admiration. Money can buy pleasure. It is also one of the most powerful sources of pain and suffering.

A certain amount of debt can be good. It can make sense to incur some debt to make money (to take out a loan to start a business), to build credit, or to make payments when liquid money is tied up in investments. You do not want debt you cannot afford, which is debt that makes no financial sense, requiring you to go into more debt to pay the interest on the first debt.

Imagine someone who, in a powerful meditation retreat, had a strong Awakening experience. If she was not at all identified with the material world and was amazed by being alive, what would be her relationship to money? Certainly it's clear she would spend money on things that were truly basic needs and might not have a great need for any other kind of money-related high. Yet she would want a safe place to live and might have relatives who need care. She could invest her money and create a budget, which might feel like a spontaneously joyous act and not a sacrifice.

Yet it wouldn't be inconsistent with Awakening for her to want to travel and explore the world. She might also want to attend an international meditation conference whose aim is to spread the benefits of meditation. So for this Awakened person money is important. It allows her to do what is most meaningful and helpful to her. We see, then, that the desire for money and Awakening are not necessarily mutually exclusive.

Wellness Inshifting Strategy:
Money.

Be aware of what money means to you and how it affects you emotionally. For example, think about whether you have an exaggerated fear that there isn't enough money, related to emotional insecurity; guilt about having too much money, because relatives, friends or needy people have less; a false sense of security, because you don't understand your investments or how much you have; fear because of debt or real needs like medical care; or an obsessive desire for more money, because (through marketing influences) you have been programmed to equate money with the "good life" of being rich and famous.

Wellness Inshifting Strategy:
Budgets and investments.

Budget, save and invest your money. Live an ordered financial life and experience greater material success and an orderly progression to freedom from money. Learn to inshift while keeping to a budget and tracking your cash flow. Learning how to make investment choices teaches wisdom, and shopping in an inshifted state shows you both self-control and spontaneity.

They may be unusual and rare, but it is still important to plan for disasters. Planning offers a sense of relief you may not even know you needed, and it's enlivening to take care of business. A person Awakening is not like the stereotyped image of the yogi sitting on a mountaintop far from civilization, wild-haired, wound in a sheet, contemplating a flower. Awakening does not require your mind to be still or empty. It requires that *you* be still and empty in your inner self. You still live in the real world, even more so. The sense of responsibility for yourself and your family and community doesn't diminish, it intensifies.

Wellness Inshifting Strategy:
Disasters.

Plan for disasters that are more likely to happen by buying supplies and getting training. Whether or not you ever use them, the preparation alone is important. Here are common disasters you should prepare for, with some of the tasks to include:

- **Injury and health-related emergencies:**
  - Learn CPR skills and first aid.
  - Buy and keep good health and long-term care insurance.

- **Weather-related emergencies relevant to your area, e.g., storms, hurricanes, floods, excess heat, sun and cold:**
  - Use sunscreen.
  - Store water and rotate the supply every six months.
  - Store dried food.

- **Geological and terrorist disasters relevant to your area. Keep these things on hand:**
  - A two-week supply of fresh water, updated every six months.
  - A two-week supply of nonperishable food.
  - A battery-operated radio.
  - A flashlight with working batteries.
  - Candles and matches.
  - An out-of-state emergency contact.
  - Relevant disaster insurance, e.g., earthquake if you live in an earthquake zone.

- **Fires:**
  - Plan an evacuation route from your house.
  - Install a fire alarm.

- Update fire safety building construction.
- Think about fire safety in using electricity and in cooking.
- Buy fire insurance.

- **Crime:**
  - Consider an alarm system or individual alarms for your home.
  - Consider bars on the windows and outside lighting if needed.
  - Educate and drill your children on appropriate behavior with strangers, rehearse it with them, and keep their fingerprints on file.

- **Driving:**
  - Keep appropriate safety equipment on board, e.g., flares, tire jack, flashlights, booster cables, first aid kit and manual.
  - Rotate and inspect tires regularly.
  - Use appropriate tires for weather conditions.

31

Moral Inshifting:
Principles and Purpose

And the righteous will rejoice ...
and be filled with happiness.

— *Hebrew Talmud (tehilim 68:4)* —

The call to service is a yearning from the heart
to live and move beyond ourselves.

—*Fredric and Mary Ann Brussat* —

In the mental hospital, I was locked like an animal in
a cage ... But in the darkness I had acquired a sense of
my own unique mission in the world. I knew then, as
I know now, that I must have been preserved for some
reason—however small, it is something that only I can
do, and it is vitally important that I do it.

— *Victor Frankl* —

Passion is energy. Feel the power that comes
from focusing on what excites you.

— *Oprah Winfrey* —

Suppose you are told some surprising news. You physician has consulted several other authorities and can definitively tell you when your life will be over. It's not immediate; for illustrative purposes, let's say it's in 10 years. How would *you* react to the concrete realization of the finality of your own end?

Depending on many factors, such as how old you are or how much you contemplate your end, you might react differently. Yet for most people who cherish their lives, according to psychiatrist Elisabeth Kübler-Ross, the definitiveness of this knowledge would lead to a process of grieving. After the initial surprise or shock and confusion, denial might pierce the natural illusion created by your mind that it will not end. Anger and disappointment may set in next, as you think, "[Expletive!] I wanted to be around longer, to do and feel so much more in this world. How can this happen to me?" Bargaining or false hope might come up right before depression: "I can't enjoy life knowing that it is going to end. I can't take the fact that I'm leaving everyone and everything I have loved and cared about."

Finally, according to Dr. Kübler-Ross, comes acceptance. What would that look like, to come to terms with the certainty, the specific inevitability of your death? How would you experience the things in your life that your mind has cherished, such as nice clothes, an ideal family, jewelry, furnishings, a great haircut? Would there be a change in you and in your attitude about life?

How would you relate to your values, moral decisions, principles and sense of purpose? Would you think more about a legacy, what you want others to remember about you? Would that change your values? Would wanting to make a difference in the world become more important than achievement at work (if they were different)? What would be a priority over spending time with family?

Recognizing your mortality is a form of moral inshifting! "Morality" is defined here as the decisions you make that further your Awakening. Compassion, empathy, mercy, humbleness, maturity and justice are all ways of experiencing and doing that cause and intensify inshifting. With this definition how would you discipline your children, supervise people, eat, organize your day, treat animals, help people less fortunate than you?

Morality comes in the form of values, principles and life purpose or mission. Values bring morality down to the level of more specific ideals, areas or issues that are important to you. They are not about choosing a silver ring over a gold one; values are about truth, family, love, honor, self-respect, comfort, material success and so on. It might be a value to look good and feel confident. However, it should be significantly important to you to list it as a "value."

 Wellness Inshifting Strategy:
Values.

Be constantly in touch with what is important to you—your values. Re-sort and reprioritize them regularly. (Use the LifePlan for this and the other exercises in this chapter.)

Principles are the rules and guidelines that bring your values to life in a practical sense, that are in your best Awakened self-interest. The "golden rule," to treat others the way you want to be treated, would fit with this definition; however, you would treat others the way you want to be treated to feel more alive just by doing so, not to gain better treatment. Ideally you will *feel* it as an inshift.

For example, think of the precepts for or against sexuality. Would rules that curtailed your sexual activity help you feel more inshifted? Your answer is about the rightness of your choice for the purpose of being inshifted. It doesn't necessarily concern the greater good of society or the rightness of a decision for some idea of morality that is handed down to you. If a decision or action lifts you toward Awakening then it will most likely be good for others, too. It isn't a great idea to act morally for some ideal if you are faking. That could be destructive to you and even to the greater good.

What about a rule to not talk to a relative who offended you? In an inshifting approach, you'd have to feel whether holding on to bitterness causes you to feel a relaxed energy or whether it drains you. You'd also have to know what helps you find inner serenity and strength—being a doormat or having a kind and bold assertiveness.

 Wellness Inshifting Strategy:

Moral imperatives.

Promote basic moral decision-making that stimulates inshifting by anticipating ahead of time that your lower brain will be affected by biases and other programming. Do this by creating moral imperatives, principles that counter immoral instincts and behavior. An example of a moral imperative is "Never use corporal punishment on my children in anger" or "Driving is not a competitive sport." Moral imperatives fit your issues and your values.

 Wellness Inshifting Strategy:

Moral decision-making.

In ambiguous situations, make moral decisions that energize your higher brain and advance you toward Awakening, a practice that naturally stimulates inshifting. Moral decision-making involves imagining each choice while even a bit inshifted. This means you are detached and in a place of clarity. The choice that lets you feel more alive and energized while calm and at peace inside may be the right choice for you. Or you may need to use the opposite criteria: the choice that most stimulates your mind, sets your thoughts racing and depletes you of energy and exhausts you is usually not right for you. Moral choice is based on your ability to inshift, although even approximating inshifting helps you better learn to do it. Making consistently "moral" choices causes you to inshift naturally.

 Wellness Inshifting Strategy:

Creative solutions.

Allow the intuitive, compassionate and logical sides of your situation to spontaneously meld, so that creative solutions emerge. Then when you feel the energy and settled feeling of a decision, you know it is right, that it is moral as we define it.

As with the other strategies, this practice leads to even more inshifting. It becomes a means to an end and an end in itself. For example, you are home at night, having worked hard all day. You have a weight problem, but you also want some comfort food like ice cream and to sit and watch TV. What should you do? Again, remember this is a moral question as I define it. It's to show you the process, not require a particular solution.

Put yourself in a state of detached awareness and experience the alternatives. You don't eat the ice cream or even watch TV, but read or spend quality time with a family member. You go to sleep feeling proud of yourself for not having the ice cream, and for doing something productive with your time. Then your mind (directed by your higher brain) imagines eating the ice cream and enjoying it while watching a great movie. This feels happy and pleasurable, and like a reward for hard work. Then your mind jumps scenes and you see yourself full of remorse because it impacts your weight and mood.

But still there is no clear inner message. There are no integrative perspectives, no new and creative solutions jumping out at you; there is only ambivalence. The answer still spells the logical choice, "no ice cream," and you feel sad and deprived.

You allow the confusion to be (allowing and fully experiencing confusion is a productive strategy for spiritual growth). You spontaneously begin to empathize with yourself. Compassion emerges for the sadness you feel. You understand more about how much you need approval from others about your weight. This deeply affects you: you value yourself and want to be good to yourself.

Opposing perspectives are allowed to live within you at the same time. You wait, and it hits you! You know the answer is right and you can trust it this time! Have as much ice cream as you want and enjoy it fully. Celebrate your existence. Make a clear, deeply resonant and realistic promise to start a more healthy diet and ride your bicycle more frequently. That will provide balance. These are things you enjoy anyway, and you have been looking for the right time to put them into practice. Your energy level rises with excitement that feels right, and brings you inner peace. You intuitively know you can trust yourself and your decision, unlike previous times when you were fooling yourself. There is no other self to fool. This is a spontaneous commitment done with love and joy.

Wellness Inshifting Strategy:

List of principles.

Keep a running list of principles that you believe in and that give you guidance and inspiration. Refer to them regularly, think of them, and use them for moral guidance.

Morality also includes discovering a passion to make a difference in the world by doing something you're good at or care about. That life purpose must be altruistic—for the good of others or other things besides your immediate self-interests.

Beware. An obsession is not the same thing as a passion. History is filled with people who followed a supposed higher calling that was clearly self-centered, mean-spirited or outright evil. Although it may have brought them immediate gratification, it was also most likely at the cost of an Awakening.

You may be obsessed with buying a particular type of trinket, but is that really a selfless, altruistic hobby? You might say that it is to make the world a more beautiful place, but perhaps it is to further your own sense of importance. This is why learning to neural inshift is crucial to wellness, and vice versa.

All the aspects of your LifePlan fall into perspective when you are in touch with your mission. If we are in touch with what motivates us on the deepest levels, with what brings us the most positive joy, with what we are best at or what naturally energizes us, we will be much more interested in furthering it by inshifting.

A *mission* fits all or most of these criteria:

• It is a broad or long-range aim.

- Its end is for the good of other people, living beings or things (including your religious beliefs) other than or more than yourself—it's altruistic.

- Its aim is to leave the world a better place, whether on a small or large scale.

- It matches your personality, talents, abilities, interests or needs.

- It is naturally enjoyable, absorbing and stimulating to you—it is a passion.

- It probably involves sacrifices that don't feel like sacrifices.

- It causes inshifting in you, and, by example, in others.

This definition raises a purpose or mission from a goal to a spiritual journey. It is a path that takes you beyond what you might be doing if you were solely living a day-to-day existence, either for your survival, to gobble up immediate pleasure or to feel psychologically safe. It pushes you beyond who you would normally be if solely concerned about yourself. It expands your heart so that you care more about the world, so that you can empathize more with people than you probably thought possible. It expands your worldview so that you experience the world, people and yourself with a broader or deeper perspective.

Wellness Inshifting Strategy:

Life's mission.

Be open to discovering your life's passion and purpose. A true mission reorients the values of your ordinary life. Your goals and daily schedule are informed by the passion for your life's purpose. The priorities you give to life's tasks are rearranged by what directly or indirectly affects your purpose, from your choice of spouse to the time you allocate to cleaning house. Even your motivation to complete tasks is increased.

32
Spiritual Inshifting:
Ancient Rites, Modern Practice

The Kingdom of Heaven is within.

— *Jesus* —

Be a lamp unto yourself.

— *Buddha* —

"Spiritual" is a term with different understandings. To some, it means something metaphysical, involving a spirit unrelated to a physical body or a spirit beyond detection by human senses or electronic equipment. Since this term carries so many preconceived notions, and this book keeps a scientific relevance, let's explore this term a bit more, using one of the most foundational laws of physics as an example.

The second law of thermodynamics says that the universe is heading to entropy, or maximal disorder. Given enough time, all matter in the universe will disperse into black and cold energy. Some believe that the only reason matter and everything else was formed, and the reason for the increasing complexity of the universe, from gases to planets, and of life on Earth, is that organized things use up energy faster. Their very complexity hastens this disorder.

That explanation defies credulity, given the unfathomable complexity of living organisms. The creative force is clearly a counterforce to entropy that has been less than adequately explained. It serves to evolve, whereas entropy destroys. With this incredible force, energy is compelled to become matter and evolve into life. When you're able to experience what Rabbi Abraham

Joshua Heschel calls a "radical amazement" at the singularity of this creative force, it Awakens you. You get the miracle of *your* existence.

Here's another way to look at spirituality from a scientific perspective. Modern quantum physics has shown that there is connectivity within the universe. If twin particles spinning in different directions are separated in space—no matter how far apart they are!—one will change its spin when its twin's spin is changed! Incredibly, what happens in one area of space can directly affect other areas long distances away, maybe everywhere! When you can somehow tune in to and be more aware of this interconnectivity, there is also a profound shift in how you normally view yourself. It furthers the dissolution of your ego. No longer do you experience yourself as a separate and distinct entity competitively struggling to thrive.

These phenomena—the creative force and connectivity—indicate that there is more to the universe than most of us are currently aware of. Clearly, there is more to our brain than most people experience as well.

Spirituality, then, can be viewed as a few things. It is the brain's remarkable ability to experience, on some level, the creative and interconnected forces. And it is the psychological and physical transformation that happens when you tune in to these forces, an Awakening to the incredible improbability and significance of your existence in each moment, and to your interconnectedness with everything around you.

Now, an explanation is due. Because the term "spiritual" has many different meanings, I prefer to use terms like "Awakening" or "higher reality." The same holds for "spiritual" strategies, which I refer to as "traditionally spiritual" strategies because they are associated with age-old spiritual and religious traditions. Even though I am not using the term "spirituality" in a classically metaphysical sense, it doesn't negate the possibility of a metaphysical or religious cause. However, acceptance of a particular religious explanation is not required for an inshift to happen.

So, what are these traditionally spiritual practices? Some are the concept of forgiveness or the practices of yoga and tai chi, two of the older spiritual practices. Then there are traditionally spiritual strategies such as meditation and prayer, humility, self-honesty, remorse and repentance, contemplative time, devotion, gratitude and sacred rituals. Traditional spirituality includes things on a higher plane such as spontaneous style and grace, seeing beauty and being romantic.

Let's discuss humility. Remember ego? It is the organizing theme of the mind that gives you the needed illusion that you are a separate person, the "I." Untamed by your higher brain, it is the cause of most if not all of your emotional unease and psychological suffering. It stays increasingly childish, defensive, arrogant, hostile, self-obsessed, selfish, fearful, isolated, lonely, scared and so on. The term "transcendence," which can be equated with Awakening, means experiencing beyond your ego. It is the central theme to inshifting, detaching, disengaging and de-identifying from a separate and self-centric view of life. That is the entryway to the ultimate, the realm of interconnectedness, realization and amazement.

 Wellness Inshifting Strategy:
Practice humility.

Practice humility in all you do, even when you are being assertive. Make efforts in your daily life to not be presumptuous, to not give absolute credence to your opinions and beliefs. Reserve some room for appropriate self-doubt in trusting your enviro-body-mind. Include humility as a key value, and in your moral decisions and principles. Being humble does not mean being unassertive or unnecessarily meek. It does mean being willing to put aside your pride, being willing to take risks with your comfort level for such things as maintaining social appearances. It means delaying your own needs (as appropriate) in favor of others. Here are some specific ways to be humble:

- Listen empathetically to people, both adults and children. Do that at least as much as, if not more than, you talk about yourself. Make a concerted effort to understand their perspectives, lives, plights, accomplishments and joys. Be willing to witness what it is like to be them before you pass judgment.

- Be more patient with others, particularly in busy or crowded circumstances, such as while driving or on public transportation. Be tolerant of the inconveniences they may cause.

- Stop arguing when it serves no real purpose besides proving how smart or righteous you are.

- Stop competing when it isn't necessary, e.g., while driving, waiting in lines, with coworkers.

- Praise others' efforts and acknowledge their accomplishments.

Self-honesty, being honest with yourself, is part of humility. In this sense, I mean it as a form of confession. Just as confessing to a priest is releasing, being honest with yourself, not denying what you know deep down is true, will help you detach and in-shift. This is also helpful to do with others you trust who won't hurt or judge you.

Self-honesty adds to your inshifting ability because most of us struggle with minds that are childlike and must be "raised," so to speak. In essence, the predominant condition of most adults is that their higher brain-controlled mind raises their lower brain-controlled mind, as if they are raising a child. For example, if you are like other people, you experience yourself as better or worse than others. It's built in to your mind in the same way instincts are built in. That is a perspective that is relatively immature, a mind-set that is associated with early stages of development.

You might think of yourself as superior to people you've never met—more understanding of issues, more enlightened, less disturbed, less evil, more important. Or you might think yourself inferior to them, less talented, less happy, less cool, more screwed up, insecure. Being honest about that is hard. The logic and dispassion that comes with inshifting can help.

Similarly, you might keep secrets, fundamental secrets about your unworthiness, lovability and abnormality, things we all believe to some degree and are ashamed of, but wouldn't be if they were exposed to the light of Awakening. Like most people, you worry that your secret will be discovered and people will see how you have been pretending to be confident, secure or happy. Almost every person standing around at that cocktail party or in your social network is feeling more or less the same way.

Don't deny that you are frail, weak, flawed and otherwise unworthy of humiliation, shunning, blame or derision. Denying these things just makes them seem more real. Accept your opinion. Validate that perspective and you will be better able to detach from these things and see them as unreal.

Wellness Inshifting Strategy:

Be honest with yourself.

Admit you have struggles, that you have a mind that is undeveloped, weak, scared and childlike. Admit it to yourself regularly and admit it to others when you feel safe. It helps you detach your outer self from your inner self, giving you wisdom and perspective.

Everyone needs contemplative time. Contemplation means to engage in introspection, to consider the past in relation to your future goals, to deepen your perspectives on your relationships and your roles, to become more in tune with your core values, to grieve the losses in your life (such as people, stages of life, pets, objects and physical abilities), to get more in tune with what you appreciate, to come closer to religious teachings and beliefs.

Contemplation can be done alone in an inspiring setting, with an organized group on retreat, or in a retreat center on your own. In any case, it should happen in a setting that tries to shut out the disturbances of daily life, somewhere different from where you normally live and work, to relieve habitual thoughts and feelings. These settings include classic settings that stimulate contemplation, such as walks along the ocean, hikes in the mountains or camping in the desert. Natural settings are conducive to deep contemplation and broad perspectives. For some people, though, taking long drives, staying at a resort or with friends or relatives where you have freedom and support may also work.

Wellness Inshifting Strategy:

Engage in periods of contemplation regularly.

Do it long enough that you feel restored, renewed (energized and settled) and enthusiastic: typically once a year for two or three days is needed.

If medically sanctioned, fasting can sometimes add an element of intensity to the experience. It may also detract from it. Regardless, healthy eating is a must during this time. Prayer or meditation also can strengthen the experience.

If you are on retreat with others, try to make the quality of this time different from that of a reunion or holiday. Keep conversations deeper and reflective of your life and future, your LifePlan and your inshifting wellness path in general. Not morose or without humor and joy, just introspective.

This is not a luxury. It is an essential part of your growth and development. It may also be central to your mental health, if stress is really getting to you or you feel stuck in life. Contemplative time, particularly for those living an urban lifestyle, can prevent stress and illness.

Personal style, artistry, grace or sensuality (as opposed to sexuality) are part of what it means to be spontaneous. Remember, spontaneity is an outgrowth of coming to the joyous realization of what it means to be alive. It's the direct result of being so inshifted that you gain an easy executive control of your mind and body.

When you're spontaneous, you're fluid in how you move and express yourself. With your senses energizing in a sensual way you feel a personal style, as when you are wearing clothes or jewelry that make you feel and look good. You carry yourself with joy and ease as well as grace and dignity.

Romance is not just for young couples in love. Romance is for everyone, whether you're young, old, male, female, macho or obsessed with getting ahead. It's part of having style and grace, of allowing your romantic feelings and playfulness to emerge. It's the antidote to self-obsession, a fun and enjoyable way to detach from your ego and appreciate the present moment. Being romantic isn't only about kissing your partner passionately, or even about your romantic relationships. It means being considerate of people and being thoughtful, being generous and playful, and feeling and expressing a sense of adventure, mystery and possibility.

Wellness Inshifting Strategy:

Be sensual, and carry yourself with style and grace.

Let it work backward in helping you inshift so you don't need to think about it, so it happens spontaneously. Make yourself aware of your body throughout the day. Carry yourself with class and style, an easy, fluid and joyous grace and dignity in whatever you do.

Sometimes wearing jewelry or attractive clothes helps create an uplifting attitude. Do this whether you are feeling great or low. Don't pass up opportunities to feel sensual enjoyment. Let yourself enjoy the feel of the chair you might be sitting in or the clothes you are wearing. Enjoy the sensations around and within you. Many sensations can be enjoyed if approached in the right way and in the right frame of mind. Think about how you enjoyed the feel of different things as a child, even if they were rough or soft, clean or dirty. Remember mud? Remember dragging your hand along a fence? Remember how you enjoyed touching, seeing or hearing new things? Open up your mind to your senses, as if you were a child again. Make it a pleasant and easy way to raise yourself to a higher reality.

 Wellness Inshifting Strategy:

Practice being romantic.

Compliment a coworker on something not work related. Chat with a store clerk. Acknowledge birthdays. Stay young at heart. See life as an adventure and mystery full of possibilities. Make family outings an adventure. View science as an unfolding and exciting mystery. See the possibilities in an old house. Let it spur you to shape your SBMA, rather than be shaped by them.

These last few aspects of spiritual inshifting may seem similar. They do overlap, and maybe are ultimately the same thing. The same holds for seeing beauty and novelty. It is part of having style and being romantic.

When I started writing this section, I was caught in a rain shower one evening. I found cover under a store awning while

I waited for the rain to slow down. At first I was impatient and anxious to go home, but then I started to notice that rain puddles were reflecting the neon signs across the street. As each raindrop splashed and splattered in the puddles, patterns of amazing psychedelic shapes and colors shifted and blended. It was beautiful. It felt like a visual massage, lifting my spirits and putting me in touch with the other sensual aspects of the night, like the cool, moist air on my face. Eventually, I decided to make a run for it, but not before I felt an immediacy nostalgia for that unique sensual, novel and artistic moment.

Wellness Inshifting Strategy:

See art and novelty everywhere.

Take time to appreciate actual art. When you are doing mundane tasks, such as walking to your car, experience the artistic aspects of where you are. You can capture artistry in what is obviously beautiful, such as a sunset, but you can also find art in less obvious places, such as in the distribution of trash in a filthy alley. You can find beauty in obscure places, such as the patterns of light running through a soda bottle, in shapes in a rug, or in the symphony of crickets, frogs and wind at night.

Experience your environment as if it were new and interesting. Look for things in familiar places that you haven't noticed before. See signs on store windows you have passed hundreds of times. See things from different angles. Watch the subtleties in changes of light. Go to a film; visit art galleries; attend concerts, theater and dance performances. Fit them into your schedule. Although some would say it is a luxury, experiencing art is a necessity.

Without obsessing over this, regularly experiencing your environment will keep you from falling prey to the habit of not noticing. It trains you in increasing awareness while energizing and relaxing you.

The topic of spontaneity by itself may seem redundant, but spontaneity is more than being fluid and freer when you're going about your life. It also involves doing things in contravention to the norm, acting freely when it is not acceptable to the culture you're in at the moment, whether it is the culture of the people in the room, your social class or civilization. When you can be spontaneous in those environments, you are liberated.

Remember, spontaneity is not the same thing as impulsivity, although it can be difficult to tell the difference. Impulsivity feels as if you are out of control, based on the programming of your SBMA rather than true needs. Spontaneity comes from powerful emotions deep within you, from your inshifted experience, from your energized higher brain that is in full awareness and control. It doesn't matter whether everyone else approves or whether it seems odd to others. Spontaneous urges feel right, moral and evolving. They're loving rather than ego-centered. You'll *know* when something within you is erupting spontaneously when you need to laugh uproariously out loud. Or you'll feel a powerful urge to hug someone or to be romantic.

Yet if you are like most people, you suppress these urges without knowing it. You might, for example, get embarrassed to give someone a hug when the moment calls for it, or be too afraid of ridicule to speak out in a public setting, even when you have strong feelings and opinions. Or you might be too self-conscious to act silly when you feel the urge, or too obsessed with work or life to call your family when you think of it.

The trick, again, is to know the difference between a spontaneous urge to act and an impulse. If you have true ambivalence or mixed feelings, then chances are it is not a spontaneous force. Making yourself do things that are not comfortable is not spontaneity.

 Wellness Inshifting Strategy:

Spontaneity.

Allow yourself to be spontaneous when it feels right, regardless of what other people think. Use your intuition as a guide to what is right. For example, if you get a funny thought in the middle of a stuffy business meeting and want to share it, but it feels inappropriate to the context of the meeting, trust that. Or, if the next thought is, "Everyone will see that I am a casual, funny person," think before speaking. That's your ego. But, if you are energized and centered, in touch with the context of the moment, the thought feels relevant, and it emerges with some energy behind it so you deeply want to share it, then allow it. To hell with what you think people will think. In an inshifted state, in that place of emptiness that transcends ego by witnessing your "self" as it witnesses the world, nothing can really psychologically hurt you.

What is sacred? There are things you hold sacred, like religious symbols, baby shoes or cherished memories. Extraordinary specialness in things and memories are what usually gets treated as sacred.

But what about ordinary moments and things? Let's revisit what we said about the astronomical, unimaginable odds of humans coming to existence; it's like finding a single grain of sand in miles of beaches. Think about the extreme improbability of you being born, less likely than you being elected president of the United States. That's extraordinary. Think again about what it means that awareness came to be, that a collection of chemicals shaped into neurons can wake up, come alive and know what's happening and then know that it knows. It's astounding.

Yet our poor lower brains can't really fathom these imponderables. Your higher brain can grasp the infinite, although without solid ideas, words and concepts, but your lower brain can't. So until you are exemplary at inshifting, focus your attention on the things and memories that are easily recognized as sacred.

Wellness Inshifting Strategy:

Create sacred things.

Create symbols, places and rituals that you can hold as sacred. If you're religious, these are ready-made. Regardless, find symbols and objects that have personal meaning and specialness for you. Put them somewhere special. Create an altar or a sacred spot, a clean space away from the usual things and places in your home (which could also be a good place to do an inshifting practice). Show your devotion to these objects at special times in whatever way feels comfortable, including thinking about them in silence, nodding your head, putting your hands together, bowing, praying, prostrating, whatever is genuine for you. Create sacred rituals around this that celebrate the other areas of wellness. Think about things that you feel reverence for and honor, such as God, historic religious figures, books, national flags or symbols, your mentors, or beautiful places, such as a mountain. Then determine to tangibly show your reverence to one or all of them regularly.

Appreciation, gratitude and the appropriate expression of remorse are traditionally spiritual ways that have been used to help people transcend ego, intensifying their experience of life. Appreciation and gratitude are other sides to experiencing sacredness in all things. This begins with the things that perhaps are not universally sacred (like a child), but which you can find appreciation for, like sacred objects. This is an easy way to accomplish great inshifting, or at least lift your mood.

We all feel remorse for something we've done. You could hardly be human and not feel sorry for something. However, remorse is not the same thing as feeling guilty. I feel guilty when I've done something wrong but didn't do anything about it, such as apologize and make amends.

Remorse is a good thing. Feeling regret keeps you humble. It contains your ego, which can grow like a weed and become toxic. Keeping open to your wrongdoings and seeking out legitimate criticism even from adversaries are really good things to do, although it can hurt and be hard to do. That's how you learn to improve, and that's how you propel your inshifting. The pain that comes from your ego is like pouring antiseptic on a wound; it hurts, but you know it's helping. You most probably acted out of ignorance or poor impulse control. By asking or remaining open to critiques you are making strides to Awakening, to being a better, more evolved person and to becoming excellent in what you do (as opposed to trying to be perfect).

So, you've gotten in touch with your remorse. What next? To

really mean what you feel, you must try to offer an apology.

Wellness Inshifting Strategy:
Appreciation and gratitude.

Make yourself a grateful person by orienting your mind to constantly appreciate things, people and events. Make appreciation a key value. Let the first thing you do in the morning and the last thing at night be to create a new item for your gratitude list, something you're newly appreciative of or something you were already grateful for, but now have a deeper appreciation for. Consider making this practice a ritual you share with your family around the dinner table.

Wellness Inshifting Strategy:

Remorse.

Allow yourself to feel remorse. Open yourself to legitimate criticism, empathize with whoever you wronged or appreciate the significance of whatever you did, but don't get mired in guilt and self-punishment.

When you invite criticism, or it comes your way whether or not you want it, it's a perfect time to practice inshifting. You will probably have a fuller view of the unhealthy parts of your ego. Detach your attention from it and experience it with distance, disengage your emotions and de-identify with it; that is, don't let it define who you are. Allow remorse to naturally emerge from deep within your mind. Fully experience it. Encourage it, even, with empathy for the person or people or animals you wronged while staying in a place of inner peace. More feelings of regret may emerge, but find a state where you don't personalize the experience, so the criticism isn't about you as a person.

If you insult someone out of anger, and you genuinely feel remorse, it may make you feel you could no sooner be Awakened than climb Mount Everest. Remember, though, that guilt and self-punishment are just more ego. They are not you, either. This kind of inshifting strategy can be very painful. Letting your ego get bruised by acknowledging mistakes may be the hardest thing you do in life. Yet confession is good for the soul.

Wellness Inshifting Strategy:

Apologize.

Apologize for your mistakes. Saying, "I'm sorry" is inadequate if it doesn't come with some statement or sign of remorse and empathy. Even though you've opened yourself to legitimate criticism or identified a mistake, felt remorse and empathy for whomever you wronged, and apologized, you're not done yet. To complete the process to help your inshifting, and to just become a wiser, more compassionate and happier person, you must make amends. You need to try to fix whatever mistake you've made, to make restitution if possible, and make a sincere pledge to yourself and to the other party to never do it again. To make restitution, you might listen to the other person and empathize with their pain. Offering flowers or gifts alone can be empty. Making amends for the wrong goes further to repair the damage and softens your ego as well. It is just too easy to buy something or make promises you don't mean or can't keep. Pledges to change are much more realistic if they are accompanied with deeply felt remorse and clear empathy.

Wellness Inshifting Strategy:

Restitution.

When you hurt someone or something, feel remorse and empathy, apologize, and try to fix the damage by making restitution if possible. Also, make a deeply motivated pledge to try not to repeat that mistake.

What about being "virtuous and kind"? When you read those words, what sort of person springs into your mind? The Mother Teresa sort, dedicated to serving humanity in dire circumstances? Is it you, in times when you've gone out of your way to be helpful, when you've been courageous enough to confess to something you did wrong or voice disagreement with most people in a meeting?

Being virtuous is an inner decency that is observable in what you do. It doesn't require sainthood, just being a decent person, fair-minded, compassionate and trustworthy as much as you can. In Chapter 26 I suggested that you write down your values and start a list of principles. That is a way to remind you about what is important and how to be virtuous and kind. In the chapter on moral wellness you learned a strategy to figure out which choices are moral, especially when there are shades of gray and complex issues.

Here we're not focused on specifics, but rather the overall connection between being virtuous and kind and how that makes it much easier to inshift in any moment. It also keeps you from being too ego-invested in outcomes. Ego creates competition at all costs. Acting for only yourself, judging without empathy, holding on to prejudices, not speaking up for the underdog—whatever keeps you from being a thoughtful and decent person—will make inshifting practically impossible. Being virtuous and kind equates to being lifted and energized, aware and grounded.

Wellness Inshifting Strategy:

Virtue and kindness.

Be a virtuous, kind, decent and thoughtful person as much as you can—even when your ego is bruised (e.g., your feelings are hurt) or your ego is inflamed (e.g., you feel greedy or sneaky). The more genuine you are in your virtue, the more it benefits you. Of course, if you act decently, the genuineness may follow. On the other hand, faking kindness is more about dishonesty than kindness. Keeping a confidence when someone could get hurt is more about virtue that comes from your ego—it's imagined instead of deeply felt. It can wear on you because it's not authentic. There's no benefit to that, and it may even be harmful. I'm not saying to be rude and push ahead in front of someone to be authentically you. Just be real. Find the caring side of you and let it out.

Feel honest and be honest. Stand up for people or animals that are being hurt in any way. Feel and be righteous. The more authentically virtuous and kind you are, the less identified with your ego you will be, and the more you'll find yourself present in each moment.

Finally we arrive at the strategy that you may have thought the whole book was going to be about—meditation. In going through the steps of inshifting you might have wondered why meditation wasn't discussed as part of the process.

The answer is simple, but profoundly important: I wanted to make it clear that neural inshifting is portable. No special conditions are required—low lights, a quiet room, incense, a bell to begin practice with and so on. You can inshift anywhere and anytime. Inshifting happens inside you, whether you are formally meditating, rolling in mud, screaming at your teammates, in crisis, waiting in line, having sex or making a presentation. Finding that inner place of presence requires that you shift a bit of energy and attention around, not run to a cushion, sit cross-legged and begin watching your breath. Realizing on a deeper level that *you exist right now* doesn't require you to stop what you're doing or thinking.

That being said, however, inshifting on the fly without regular practice is tricky perhaps—at first. Various forms of meditation are usually critical to help you really learn the skills of inshifting. And there are Hindu-based meditations, such as Transcendental Meditation and yoga. Meditation is a deliberate path inward (as opposed to the accidental path of Awakening) to discover your higher self and to Awaken your brain. I'm most familiar with the mindfulness meditation schools, from which neural inshifting arose.

There are many different ways to practice mindfulness meditations, including both secular and religious settings and rituals.

Formal settings and rituals, body and mind postures, a meditation teacher and the company of other meditators are enormously helpful.

Formal neural inshifting requires a delicate balancing act.
You will use your mind to instruct yourself on what to do as you
work your way up the steps. But then you must learn to let go
of self-instructions and self-assessments. You may ask, "If I don't
talk to myself the whole time I'm inshifting, how do I tell myself
that I'm succeeding?" That's a crucial question. I think it's a point
where I'm sure even advanced meditators get tripped up.

There is a Zen parable that may help you understand this
point. The master sees his disciple trying very hard to be a good
meditator. When he sees his disciple polishing a tile, he asks him
how, by polishing the tile, he can turn it into a jewel. The disciple, obviously confused, asks, "How, master, can I turn a tile
into a precious stone?"

The master then asks how the disciple can learn to Awaken
by trying to be something other than who he is. At that, the disciple has a great Awakening.

Self-coaching and self-assessment is not being you—it's
thinking about being you. If you rely on it, it takes you away
from just being yourself. That's really all you are trying to do with
inshifting: learning to be your natural higher self.

At what point do you let go of self-coaching and self-assess-
ing, which embody a continuous drive for improvement? At
what point do you accept everything about a moment, including
the idea that you are not meditating well enough, so that you can
enter a state of openness where you just know and just are?

There need to be some verbal directions and assessments on
one's meditational inshifting. Self-instructions and coaching are
necessary to begin and sustain inshifting, to some degree. This is
a key balance you will be more directly faced with in your meditational inshifting practice. At some point, early on, you have to
let go of that self-coaching. Or perhaps it doesn't leave as much as

it is detached from and de-identified with. You eventually learn to feel what it means to be you, so that you don't need the instructions on how to be you. You just naturally *are*. Make sense?

So, at every step, in the beginning at least, instruct and assess, but from a place of detachment. It's like counting your breaths. You can do it from an inner place.

Here's another element that you will face in a meditational inshifting practice: faith. While you inshift, faith keeps you motivated. Faith means accepting that what I am telling you in this book is true until you can grasp it for yourself. Faith helps you deal with another aspect of formal neural inshifting: doubt. Deep doubt stays with you in the early years of your practice, like a shadow. It is part of your mind's programming. Learn to see it for what it is and detach so that it doesn't drag you down.

Wellness Inshifting Strategy:

Formal inshifting.

Develop a daily formal or meditational inshifting practice. It should mainly be a sitting practice that includes some walking or running. It should come with rituals before and after that mark it as a significant time, such as ringing a bell, bowing, saying a prayer, lighting incense and so on. I ring a bell, because the energy of the sound pierces into my Point X and stimulates it. It also cuts through my internal talking. I encourage you to find your own rituals that support inshifting and to find a suitable teacher and community of fellow meditators as well.

Create a sacred space. Find a room that you can use at a regular time each day that is comfortable for you, not too cold or too warm, very tidy, with a minimum of ongoing noise and few interruptions, e.g., telephone ringing. Find a spot in the room that is cozy and safe, where you can put a special mat or rug.

Find either a special and comfortably firm chair or firm cushions to sit on. The chair or cushions should support you in sitting upright (see Figure 17). Get an alarm clock with a gentle signal, such as chimes or nature sounds. Eventually, this spot will become more sacred to you. Just being in this space should help you start inshifting right away.

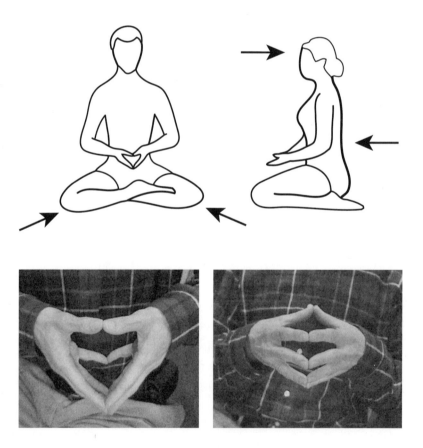

Figure 17. Posture for meditational inshifting

Create the right physical and mental posture for balanced energy. If you are flexible, sit cross-legged on cushions so that your knees can touch the ground. Otherwise, a cushioned but firm chair works, but only if you can sit in it and place your feet firmly on the floor.

Sit up straight with the small of your back curved slightly forward, your thighs pointed down at about 45 degrees and your head erect (see Figure 17). This straightens the spine. An erect spine is highly energizing to the brain. That is the first thing you can do to increase your energy level.

Rest your hands comfortably on your lap, fingers touching on both hands (see Figure 17). In this hand posture, with thumbs lightly touching, the gentle vibration between your thumbs acts like a gauge of alertness—too light and not touching at all and you may be too distracted or relaxed; too firm and you may be trying too hard.

Sit as still as you possibly can! This is important, because the urge to move is one of the aspects of your SBMA that you want to detach from. Plus, body movements stimulate your mind and make it harder to detach. The more active your SBMA, the more it can grab your attention. That can drain your energy before its gets to your higher brain.

Sit up straight and gently balance yourself on the edge of a chair or in cross-legged or kneeling positions. Relax all your nonworking muscles while gently sitting erect and balanced.

Now you're ready to begin the core neural inshifting part of the meditation practice. Begin the steps of inshifting. Here's a summary.

- Experience energy from SBMA, release it to relax and draw it into your head to stimulate you.

- A gentle oculofocus uses your eyes to concentrate energy in Point Y, as well as to soften your attention on and loosen immediate control of SBMA.

- Draw energy farther in to Point X, using it to detach your attention (indirect awareness) from SBMA and let go of immediate control.

- Stretch your attention farther in to discover a place of inner openness and inner gentle power from which your SBMA is seen as an independent whole, vivid, novel and less real.

- Stretching your attention even farther in, find a more intensive experience of being alive in each singular moment. This is where your inner strength becomes the peak of conscious choice and authentically spontaneous action and intuition.

In this meditative practice of neural inshifting you sit with an erect posture, in a quiet and special space, with your fingers touching and your eyes open and cast down in front of you, at the same time every day.

Here's the next element. Breathing.

Just like you let go of controlling other aspects of body and mind, you also stop controlling your breath. Without locking attention on it, the depth and rate of your breath will be what it is, and eventually it'll start to slow. It may even slow to a stop and seem like an eternity before it starts again. (You don't need to control it even then, because you won't suffocate. I am still occasionally thrown by the sensation of my breath seeming to stop for the longest time. That's an excellent opportunity to learn inshifting.)

As you are aware of your breath (and everything else) in this practice, start off by counting your breaths. Count either exhalations or inhalations. How can you count your breaths while you're detached from your mind? You can direct your mind from an inner place, from a higher you. Again, I don't know how that works in the brain to control thoughts, feeling and actions without thinking. You just can. As you count your breaths, use that to stay tuned to the sensation of Point X, the experience of being detached, and let go.

When you get to 10, start over again. When you lose track and get absorbed into your mind (and you will, over and over again), come back to counting your breaths and appreciate how good it feels to come back. That way you won't feel frustrated by the process of self-learning.

This concludes the many wellness strategies to which you have been introduced. There are dozens of them. Even with a well-used LifePlan you can only do so much to practice all of these strategies at the same time. Even with an organization devoted to NWI, you would need a good deal of help to bring all these strategies to use in your life. Just do what you can, when you can. And most of all, enjoy getting well and the feeling of Awakening your brain.

Afterword:
The Journey to Awakening

I feel clean.
I feel free.
I feel ready to live every day with zest, by choice!
I am delighted by the adventure of each moment.
I feel as though I have just awakened from a restless,
disjointed dream. Everything looks different!
The world no longer rides heavily on my back.
It is under my belt.
I turned a somersault and swallowed it.
I am no longer restless.
At last I have what I want.

— Anonymous, Kapleau —

This book is part of my own journey of self-discovery. As I have been writing it to teach you how to Awaken from the slumber of ordinary consciousness, I have been teaching myself.

Think about this universal state I call Awakening. Think how wonderful it is that people from both religious and secular walks of life have been able to reach such exceptional states of experience. Think how we all can find a life of contentment, with moments of ecstasy, profound inner peace, insight, maturity and exceptional abilities.

My own glimpses of Awakening have been like standing on a bridge looking in both directions. I can see two sides of myself, two radically different landscapes. On one side there are my usual stressors, struggle and dysfunction. On the other is a relaxed and vibrant well-being from inshifting that often includes an amazing realization of the world and me in it as fresh and new.

There are people who go through life feeling fully alive and Awakened from the programmed reality they have been raised in. The rest of us struggle through life more asleep than awake. All that can change for you with the practice of neural-wellness inshifting (NWI).

When were the significant times in your life when you were more fully aware and alive? These are often memorable times, like the first glimpse of your baby's face. You can recall many details of those moments because you were energized and taking it all in. You didn't need a lot of processing.

People who can experience much of their lives like that, alert and aware, have learned how to be aware without being controlled by their mind, or lower brain. They experience outside the influence of their habits of thinking and believing, beyond self-reference points, without being affected by their body drives or sense triggers. They learned a clear way of "seeing" that makes their experience of everything more vivid and alive, with insight into people and the universe that penetrates the illusion created by their lower brain areas.

As you've seen in this book, learning to make the best use of your brain does not require you to struggle with confusion, metaphysical ideas or abstract philosophy. Looking at ancient wisdom and practices from the modern science-based viewpoint presented here can make the journey easier and less stressful, as gratifying as any special state you may be hoping for.

Each of our journeys is unique, with unexpected twists and turns. The approach to the skill of neural inshifting is as individual as a fingerprint. A purposeful path to Awakening requires some suffering and struggle to propel you out of a state of intense conditioning that denies self-awareness. Awakenings may be gradual *or* sudden, slight *or* profound, and may build slowly through struggle. Sometimes those who struggle the hardest are building the greatest potential for a stronger realization.

Anyone who relies heavily on thinking will find challenges in their neural inshifting. This is probably the most common reason why people who meditate don't find higher realization, and why most people have not learned these skills. Our busy lives keep us occupied in the details of each moment, rather than the transcendence of our experience.

Neural inshifting is easier and can happen more naturally when it is enhanced with multiple wellness practices geared to it. It's essential to build your own resources to support your practice, from professional guidance to a like-minded community gathered together in a conducive place to practice these skills and strategies. I could have benefited from an organization and a location that offered these things, which is why I've created SatoriWest Center for Advanced Living and Wellness: The Life-Club. To make significant strides in their journey most people need to belong to a comprehensive organization that supports, encourages, educates and provides professional assistance, retreats and a place for daily wellness practices.

NWI will challenge you in many ways. Some of them you *will* meet on your own, some you *will* find others to support you, and some you *will* need an organization that offers professional guidance to help you. Expect frustration and confusion. This is an inevitable part of the process.

However, the benefits are profound! The wellness aspects of inshifting have the indirect benefit (besides enhancing neural inshifting) of contributing to your health and emotional stability, the quality of your relationships, the material success and organization of your life, and your ability to find fulfilling work and pastimes that have passion, purpose and meaning. There may be nothing more vital to the quality of this one life you get to have.

Yet no benefit is greater than achieving a true Awakening. Awakening is the apex of existence. Once Awakened, even a bit, even for a second, you'll understand how shallow and meaningless your life was without it.

NWI is the approach that makes this stage of life, this level of development, this degree of maturity and fulfillment possible. It is the fundamental blueprint to the next stage of human evolution.

This is your opportunity to soar beyond the surface of your potential. This is your chance to work your brain to its fullest extent for peace, happiness and meaning. This is how you can Awaken your brain to a new world, heal yourself and transform your life.

If this book motivates you to make the journey and guides you along the path of self-discovery, then it will be a success. Its task will be complete. And I will consider myself lucky indeed.

Glossary

Awakening: The effect of inshifting that comes after Step 5 is achieved and sustained. Also known variously as enlightenment, nirvana, cosmic consciousness, heaven within and paradise on Earth, each depicting a different aspect of that level of experience and behavior. The term Awakening depicts more of the arousal aspects of a higher level of consciousness as it exists on a continuum with sleep and wakefulness.

Awareness: The function that tells you that something is happening. There are separate awarenesses on each side of the brain in each cerebral hemisphere. Awareness merely implies that an experience was registered somewhere in the brain, even if there was an effort to remember it later on.

Cerebral hemispheres: The two halves, right and left, of the outer layers of the human brain. These outer layers are involved in higher level functioning, such as speech and intellectual processing.

Choice: The ability to decide a course of action using reflective awareness.

Consensus trance: Coined by psychologist George Gurjieff, this term depicts the "ordinary level of reality" of most people who are effectively put in a culturally consistent trance-like state. In this state, people are rendered hyper-suggestible in experiencing and behaving the way that society programs and conditions them to experience and behave.

Context: The acute experience of perspective that comes with reflective awareness. It is the experience that tells you, for instance, that this moment is but one of many moments in a longer life, or that any event or circumstance can be experienced in relation to the wider framework of its antecedents and ramifications. The more acute experience of context comes about as the result of an acute reflective awareness and neural inshifting Step 5.

Different types of reality: This is the vertical progression of lower to higher brain functioning found in various levels of reality. The representative sample of levels of reality (and hence, experience and behavior) depicted in this book are: "dreaming," "something's wrong with your brain," "willingly suspended," "day dreaming," "ordinary, relative" and "Awakened." The vertical progression of reality shows more of the arousal features of the neurosoteriological interactions between higher and lower brain areas.

Ego: The property of the mind that allows the brain to identify itself, and that causes the brain to experience itself as significant to events, either in the middle of events or in the outside of events looking in. When this function is unchecked by the insight of awareness, it inflates into a strong force that automatically acts to strengthen itself, as in "egocentric" or "egotistical." Is used synonymously with "the mind's I."

Higher Brain: Refers to the aspects of the human brain that are responsible for the highest aspects of human functioning: awareness, reflective awareness, volition, conscious choice and future planning. The higher brain is hypothesized to be the interaction of symmetrical mechanisms on each side of the brain: the orbitofrontal prefrontal cortex and the posterior parietal lobule (which are hypothesized to endow each other with awareness) as they are coordinated by the thalamus and stimulated by the reticular activating system.

Immediacy nostalgia: The wispy and pleasant feeling of nostalgia for what is happening right now that is appreciated in a new way, which comes with greater reflective awareness and neural inshifting Step 5.

Inshifting: The process of accessing your higher brain, whether done explicitly in neural inshifting or by wellness-based inshifting or both.

LifePlan for Awakening: Also called LifePlan. The instrument used to coordinate one's life and the various wellness-based inshifting strategies. This is a wellness strategy in itself, because it helps the reader get in better touch with his values and principles in the context of time and life management.

Lower Brain: This is hypothesized to be the myriad parts of the brain that are not "higher brain." The lower brain areas working together have all the capability in humans to function on a basic level in dealing with momentary exigencies, i.e., rudimentary thinking, problem-solving, reacting to stimuli and events, and sensory recognition. The less the higher brain is available to be used by the brain in general, the more basic and dysfunctional the lower brain is in processing situations. In general, the lower brain consists of the interactions within and between its SBMA.

Mind: A tool of the brain to organize information processing, decisions and actions.

Neural inshifting: The method used to explicitly and directly access your higher brain and its potential. It has five steps that are centered around accessing Point X, both as an experiential focal point of reference and as a locus of control. The first two steps show how Point X can be more readily experienced, i.e., in how energy is manipulated within the brain and how the eyes are used to that end. The third step shows how when Point X is accessed there is a de-identification and detachment from the information of the SBMA. The fourth step shows what happens subjectively and behaviorally when Point X is accessed for even a brief period of time, i.e., the universe of experience becomes more whole, vivid, more novel and less real-seeming in comparison to an inner openness that is silent and still, while behaviorally you become more grounded and strong. The last step shows what happens when you can access Point X even longer: subjectively there is the experience of amazement at being more acutely reflectively awareness (a ROYAL Now experience), as well as becoming more spontaneous and authentic as you interact with events with greater awareness and easy deliberateness.

Neural-wellness inshifting (NWI): Also called NWI. The overall approach to inshifting that combines neural inshifting with wellness-based inshifting. It is the optimal way to become Awakened.

Neurosoteriology: The original model of how the brain works, in the levels of interaction between the higher and lower brain. The model states that the higher and lower brain areas are in a reciprocal relationship. The more the lower brain dominates, the less the higher brain functions, so that experience and behavior conform to the dictates of the programming and hardwiring of the lower brain. The more the higher brain is in force, the less influence the lower brain has on experience and behavior, so that experience and behavior are more conscious and deliberate. Neurosoteriology shows a horizontal progression of four levels from lower to higher brain functioning. The term "neurosoteriology" denotes how the brain (neuro) is able to reach what has been referred to as spiritual states (depicted in the term "soteriology," or the study of salvation, Awakening or higher states of consciousness). There is also a vertical progression from lower to higher brain functioning found in the levels of reality.

Oculofocus maneuver or technique: The channeling of arousal energy with the use of your eyes, to an area that is perceived to be inside your head behind your eyes.

Point X: A perceived area within the head—behind the eyes and between the ears (either slightly above or below)—within the location where one normally thinks and imagines. This is the inner reference point and inner center of control that corresponds to the explicit use of the higher brain.

Pyschospirituality: What has been previously known as a spiritual experience—such as a heightened sense of connectivity with the universe, a state of profound meaning and appreciation, an experience of timelessness, the transcendence of personalized perspectives—being understood as a phenomenon of the brain and/or mind.

Reflective awareness: Also known more popularly as self-awareness (a term largely avoided in this book because of a possible confusion with an awareness of a self-identity). This is the function of the brain that tells you that you are being aware at the moment. Other aspects of this or other ways to refer to this are: knowing *that* you know, knowing *what* you know, knowing *that* you are aware, being aware of being aware, and knowing that you are alive. Reflective awareness happens in the context of each unique moment. It is hypothesized to be a function of the awareness of each cerebral hemisphere working together in synchrony, like stereoscopic vision.

Reticular activating system (RAS): A tangle of nerve roots that extend off of the main spinal cord neurons whose function is to arouse the brain into awareness.

ROYAL: Realization of Your Aliveness.

SBMA: Stands for "senses, body states, mind and actions." Used interchangeably with "the lower brain," "mind," and "outer you," this is a more complete description of all the elements that make up the parts of you that are other than your inner you or higher brain. It is the sum total of everything you can sense through your vision, hearing, touch, taste and smell. It includes all your body states and drives, such as fatigue, sexual drives, feeling ill, restlessness and hyperactivity. It also includes all of your mind activity, such as emotions, thoughts, internal images, beliefs, attitudes, even your sense of "self," or the perception of being the center of your world or on the outside of it. It also includes your actions and reactions that you make either by a less-than-fully aware choice or reflexively.

Spirituality: In this book, spirituality is seen from the perspective of a science-based understanding of the brain—a psychospirituality or neurospirituality, so to speak. For instance, the heightened awareness of the interconnectivity of the universe, the ecstatic experience of presence and of the sacredness of things and people, and the experience of profound meaning in existence are all viewed as aspects of a brain that has its higher brain fully accessed. These descriptions do not require religious cosmologies or explanations, nor do they negate them. They are merely empirical observations.

Thalamus: The thalamus is a grouping of nerve cells (ganglia of nerve cells) that are involved in relaying nervous system information to the cerebral cortex and within the cerebral cortex.

Web of wellnesses: The synergistic effect of all the wellness-based in-shifting strategies used at approximately the same time to both improve the overall success of each area separately and to cause an inshift.

Wellness-based inshifting: The various strategies that are used within the six global universes of wellness (physical, mental, social, cultural, moral and traditionally spiritual) used to make inshifting happen naturally or to make neural inshifting easier to learn.

Volition: This term is used synonymously with will, conscious action or deliberateness. It implies action or thought that results from higher levels of awareness or even reflective awareness.

Bibliography

Airola, Paavo. *How to Get Well.* Health Plus Publishers. Sharewood, OR. 1974.

Andrews, Lewis. *To Thine Own Self Be True: The Relationship Between Spiritual Values and Emotional Health.* Doubleday. New York. 1987.

Bloom, Floyd E. In Ed., L. R. Squire. *Fundamental Neuroscience.* Academic Press. San Diego, CA. 2003.

Borcherdt, Bill. *You Can Control Your Feelings: 24 Guides to Emotional Wellbeing.* Professional Resource Press. Sarasota, FL. 1993.

Brussat, Fredric and Mary Ann. *Spiritual Literacy.* Touchstone. New York. 1996.

Bucke, Richard M. *Cosmic Consciousness.* Citadel Press. Secaucus, NJ. 1961.

Capra, Fritjof. *The Tao of Physics: An Exploration of the Parallels between Modern Physics and Eastern Mysticism.* Shambhala Publications. January 2000.

Coveney, Peter, and Highfield, Roger. *Frontiers of Complexity: The Search for Order in a Chaotic World.* Fawcett Columbine. New York. 1995.

Covey, Stephen, Merrill, Roger and Merrill, Rebecca. *First Things First.* Simon and Schuster, New York. 1996.

Crick, Francis. *What Mad Pursuit: A Personal View of Scientific Discovery.* Basic Books. 1990.

Csikszentmihalyi, Mihalyi. *Flow.* Harper and Row. New York. 1990.

Das, Surya. *Awakening the Buddha Within.* Broadway Books. New York. 1997.

Elliott, H. Chandler. *The Shape of Intelligence: The Evolution of the Human Brain.* Scribner. New York. 1969.

Ellis, Albert and Harper, Robert. *A New Guide to Rational Living.* Prentice-Hall. Englewood Cliffs, New Jersey. 1975.

Etzioni, Amitai. *The Spirit of Community.* Touchstone Books. New York. 1993.

The Forbes Book of Business Quotations: Thoughts on the Business of Life. Ted Goodman, Ed. Black Dog and Leventhal Publishers. New York. 1997.

Frankl, Victor. *The Unconscious God.* Simon and Schuster. New York. 1975.

Fuhrman, Joseph. *Fasting and Eating for Health.* St. Martin's Press. New York. 1995.

Gurjieff, George. *Beelzebub's Tales to His Grandson.* Harcourt, Brace. New York. 1950. (Reprinted 1993)

James, William. *The Varieties of Religious Experience.* The New American Library. New York, NY. 1958.

Jaynes, Julian. *The Origin of Consciousness in the Breakdown of the Bicameral Mind.* Houghton-Mifflin. Boston. 1976.

Haddock, Frank. *The Power of Will.* J P Tapley Co. New York. 1907.

Horowitz, Martin. *States of Mind.* Plenum Medical Book Co. New York. 1987.

Howard, Vernon. *Pathways to Perfect Living.* Parker Publishing. Pine, AZ. 1969.

Howard, Vernon. *The Mystic Masters Speak: A Treasury of Cosmic Wisdom.* New Life Foundation. Pine, AZ. 1974.

Kapleau, Phillip. *The Three Pillars of Zen.* Anchor Books. Garden City, NY. 1965.

Levine, Stephen. *A Gradual Awakening.* Anchor Books. Garden City, NY. 1979.

Meslam, M-Marcel. *Principles of Behavioral Neurology.* FA Davis. Philadelphia. 1885.

Miller, Timothy. *How to Want What You Have.* Henry Holt and Co. New York. 1995.

Nanamoli, Bhikkhu. *The Path of Purification: Visuddhimagga.* Buddhist Publication Society. Sri Lanka. 1956.

Oliver, Mary. "The Summer Day," from *New and Selected Poems.* Beacon Press. Boston. 1992.

Ornstein, Robert. *The Nature of Human Consciousness.* Viking Press. New York. 1973.

Pelletier, Kenneth. *Toward a Science of Consciousness.* Celestial Arts. Berkeley. 1978.

Pierce, R.V. *The People's Common Sense Medical Advisor in Plain English.* Buffalo, New York. 1895.

Pizzorno, Joseph. *Total Wellness: Improve Your Health by Understanding Your Body's Healing System.* Prima Publishing. Rockland, CA. 1996.

Russell, W. Richie. *Explaining the Brain.* Oxford University Press. London. 1975.

Sheng-Yen. *Getting the Buddha Mind.* Dharma Drum Publications. Elmhurst, NY. 1982.

Sherrington, Charles. *The Integrative Action of the Nervous System.* Yale University Press. New York. 1947.

Smith, Hyrum. *The Ten Natural Laws of Successful Time and Life Management: Proven Strategies for Increased Productivity and Inner Peace.* Warner Books. New York. 1995.

Suzuki, Shunryu. *Zen Mind, Beginner's Mind.* Weatherhill, Inc. New York. 1970.

Tart, Charles. *Waking Up: Overcoming Obstacles to Human Potential.* Shambhala Publications. Boston. 1986.

Tolle, Eckhart. *A New Earth: Awakening to Your Life's Purpose.* Penguin Group. New York. 2005.

Tolle, Eckhart. *The Power of Now.* New World Library. Novato, CA. 1997.

Walen, Susan, DiGiuseppe, Raymond and Dryden, Windy. *A Practitioner's Guide to Rational-Emotive Therapy.* Oxford University Press. New York. 1992.

Walsh, Roger. "The Consciousness Disciplines and the Behavioral Sciences: Questions of Comparison and Assessment." *American Journal of Psychiatry.* 137: 663-673. 1980.

Welwood, John. *Toward a Psychology of Awakening.* Shambhala Publications. Boston. 2000.

Wilber, Ken, Engler, Jack, and Brown, Daniel. *Transformations of Consciousness.* Shambhala Publications. Boston. 1986.

About the Author

Jeff Skolnick, MD, PhD, is a diplomate of the American Board of Psychiatry and Neurology and clinical assistant professor of psychiatry at the University of Washington. He has advanced training in neuropsychology and a doctorate in Natural Health. He began studying Zen and other meditation practices in 1980, and has been doing a daily form of meditation ever since. Recently, he founded the SatoriWest Center for Advanced Living and Wellness in Seattle, Washington, where its LifeClub provides support, guidance and community for people learning and practicing neural-wellness inshifting. He lives in Seattle with his two children.